READING 8

FOR YOUNG CATHOLICS

THINKING SKILLS WORKBOOK

Executive Editor: Dr. Mary Kay Clark
Editors: Seton Staff

Printed in the United States of America.

Seton Press
1350 Progress Drive
Front Royal, VA 22630

Phone: 540-636-9990
Fax: 540-636-1602

For more information, visit us on the Web at www.setonpress.com.
Contact us by e-mail at counselors@setonpress.com.

ISBN: 978-1-60704-110-8

Cover: *The Vision of Joan of Arc,* Jules Bastien-Lepage

DEDICATED TO THE

SACRED HEART OF JESUS

READING 8 FOR YOUNG CATHOLICS

THINKING SKILLS WORKBOOK

CONTENTS

READING 8 FOR YOUNG CATHOLICS

Thinking Skills Workbook

INTRODUCTION

Everyone loves a good story! Think of all the times and places stories are told: in the Bible, at bedtime, around the dinner table, during office coffee breaks, in political speeches, and over the phone. Literature is enjoyable because it tells stories.

On a practical level, this workbook will develop the thinking skills of observation, comprehension, and synthesis. These skills can be used in everyday life, for example, in conversation with others, while watching or reading the news, to notice subtle details about our environment, and so on. The habit of careful and observant reading will help you to make accurate judgments about the world around you.

On a deeper level, though, literature presents basic truths about the human condition. The human condition refers to all the aspects of living as a human, such as love, loyalty, friendship, ambition, joy, sorrow, fear, mortality, and honor. Good literature can help us understand ourselves better, but in order for it to do so, we must read well. So this workbook develops the student's ability to read, specifically, to ask questions about a text, notice details and patterns within it, and develop a deeper understanding of it. What truths does a particular story or poem present? How does it present them? Answering these questions not only makes literature more enjoyable, it provides valuable lessons about the world and how to live the Christian life.

By encouraging good reading and thinking skills, this workbook will help the student appreciate what is true, good, and beautiful about words, about stories and, ultimately, about reality.

TEACHING TIPS

For each lesson, the student should follow the procedure outlined below.

1. Read and enjoy the story.
2. If there are any words that you do not understand, look them up in a dictionary. Which definition makes the most sense in the context of the story?
3. Read through the exercise questions and review the story to answer them.
4. After completing the assigned questions, read the story again. Do you have a deeper appreciation of it than the first time you read it?

The stories for this workbook's lessons are written by established, exemplary authors. You can find their works on the Internet or in your local library. If you enjoy a particular story, you might like to read more stories, novels, and poetry by the author! However, parents need to read the other works first to ensure that they are appropriate.

St. Joan d'Arc

This workbook also contains a chapter story about the life of St. Joan d'Arc. Its chapters are divided among the lessons, with brief questions about each chapter.

KEY CONCEPTS

The questions for each story will be divided into three sections: characterization, plot, and theme. These concepts are discussed below. As you read about these terms and then **apply them in the exercises**, please remember the following points.

- We separate characterization, plot, and theme for the sake of discussion, but they are intertwined within the story. For example, the kind of person a character is (characterization) will affect the way he acts (plot).
- Literature is not a formula, like $a + b = c$. Think of the definitions given here as general guidelines. A plot structure in one story will be different from that of another.

CHARACTERIZATION

Characterization is the method by which an author brings his characters to life.

An author presents his characters in several ways, such as physical description, the character's own thoughts, words, and actions, what other characters and the narrator say about him, and how other characters react to him in the story. By taking notice of these details, a good reader can come to understand the character. A full understanding of character might consider the following issues.

1. Physical description – Tall, short, or average height? Beautiful or ugly? The physical description gives you a visual image of the character, but it can also provide insight into the character's deeper attributes. For example, John Doe's shifting eyes, slouching shoulders, and untucked shirt could indicate that he is lazy.
2. Personality traits or character traits – These are a character's intrinsic qualities, such as intelligence or bashfulness. Temporary emotional reactions like fear or sorrow are not character traits.
3. Morality – How does the character behave? To analyze his moral life, consider what he chooses to do with his natural gifts and with his situation. A moral virtue requires the character's decision to behave for the sake of a greater good than himself; a moral vice shows that he has chosen to act against a greater good. Personality traits require no such choice; they are at the service of one's morality. For example, intelligence is not a moral virtue, because no one chooses to be intelligent. Still, a person could use his intelligence morally (help others, serve God) or immorally (increase self-pride, further an evil purpose). Some moral virtues: mercy, humility, or trust in God.
4. Motivation – What does the character want? Why does he want it? Why does he behave the way he does? For instance, he might like to do puzzles because they challenge his mind.
5. Consistency – According to how a character is portrayed, are his actions believable? Is he true to character? If Jane Doe is usually very generous with her money and belongings, but suddenly refuses to share any of her birthday cake, we could say her one incident of selfishness is inconsistent with her overall generous character.
6. Does the character change? The main character in a good piece of fiction may undergo some change, usually in his internal life (morality, understanding of the world, and so on). For instance, does he change from fearful to brave?

When you are asked to write a character sketch, remember that character refers to the interior, stable qualities that cause a person to act the way he does, such as bravery, truthfulness, or generosity. A person's actions are not the same as his character or character traits, although they flow from it and serve to illustrate it. You may include examples of a person's actions in your character sketch, but be sure also to state the character traits that they illustrate.

PLOT

Plot is not simply a sequence of unconnected events, but is rather a causal sequence of events. To describe the plot of a story, one must not only list the events that happened, but include an explanation of what caused an event, of how and why one event led to another. To take a very simple example, the statement "The brave knight conquered his opponent; later, he married the princess," could not be a good plot description; it is simply a statement of two events. On the other hand, if one wrote, "Two brave knights were in love with a beautiful princess. They fought a duel, and the winner married his lady love," this could be a good plot description, because it explains the connection between the events.

When discussing plot, then, we are looking especially for the reasons that characters do what they do. Characters are motivated from within by emotions such as love, hate, fear, pride, or a sense of honor. Usually there is some situation or event in the story that arouses the emotions of a character and causes him to act. Thus, in the example above, the two knights come into conflict because each loves the princess and neither will let her go without a fight. Whenever you see a character in a story doing something out of the ordinary, try to identify the situation that has prompted him to act, and the nature of the emotion that he feels.

In all good stories, these motivating factors result in a **conflict** of some sort. There are four basic categories into which all **conflicts** fall:

1. *Man versus man.* For example, remember the two knights who fight for the princess's hand. Here, each knight loves the princess and tries to prevent the other from marrying her.
2. *Man versus self.* In this type of conflict, a person struggles against a flaw in his own character, or seeks the truth about himself. As an example of the first instance, suppose that a boy sees a woman drop a twenty-dollar bill from her purse as she walks out of a store. He picks up the money and is torn between doing the right thing (giving the money back) and keeping the money for himself. The second type of man versus self conflict might be the story of a young man who joins the army in a time of war in order to prove to himself that he has courage.
3. *Man versus nature.* For example, a man who is lost in the wilderness must contend with impersonal forces, such as hunger, thirst, wild animals, harsh weather conditions, or the pressure of time itself.
4. *Man versus society.* For example, a young black girl experiences racial prejudice and must struggle to overcome the hostility she faces.

There are often two or more conflicts present in a literary work. For instance, a man versus nature conflict often goes hand-in-hand with a man versus self conflict, since physical hardship usually involves a test of virtue as well. Likewise, it is probable that any story containing a man versus society conflict will also involve a man versus man conflict, since society is made up of men. One conflict, however, usually stands out as being more important than the rest when we consider the main idea that the author is trying to illustrate.

To further understand plot, notice how the events of a story build on each other, in a cause-effect relationship. The plot pattern generally follows this sequence:

- Exposition— also called introduction; this part of the story introduces characters and the conflict; it can be very brief.
- Conflict— the main conflict extends throughout the story; it can be seen near the beginning and is not usually resolved until near the end.
- Rising action— the events that increase the conflict, complicate it, and bring it to a point in which it must be decided
- Climax— the point in which the conflict is decided; one side wins; clear outcome of the story
- Falling action and resolution— other problems in the story are solved or explained; author ties up any loose ends

Notice that it is impossible to discuss plot apart from character. Just as we learn about the nature of the characters by observing what they do and why they do it (i.e., the plot), so we learn about plot by watching the characters as they act according to their natures.

THEME

The theme of a literary work is the main idea that a writer is trying to get across to the reader, usually an insight about life or human nature. Now, it is true that an author could come right out and state the theme in a single sentence and be done with it, but that would not be very satisfying for either the author or the reader, and it definitely would not be literature. The purpose of a literary work is to expand upon the theme and illustrate it using specific characters and events, thereby bringing the main idea home to the reader with greater force. In other words, the author does not simply state his idea, but rather he tries to show the reader the truth of his idea by giving a concrete example of it.

An example will help to illustrate this. The most basic type of story is the fable, which is a tale with a very clear theme, usually stated at the end in the form of a moral. Most students will be familiar with the fable of "The Boy Who Cried Wolf":

> There once was a shepherd boy who grew bored watching his flock of sheep near a village. Three or four times he brought the villagers out by crying "Wolf! Wolf!" When his neighbors came out to help him, he was much amused, and laughed at their angry faces.
>
> The wolf, however, did truly come at last. The shepherd boy cried out in alarm, "Please, come and help me! The wolf is killing the sheep!" This time the villagers, ashamed at having been fooled several times already, paid no attention to his cries, and no one came to help him. The wolf proceeded to destroy and scatter the sheep.
>
> The moral of the story: "A liar will not be believed, even when he is telling the truth."

It would be too vague to say that the theme of the story is "One should never lie." This is indeed part of the message of the story, but it takes no account of the events therein and the particular type of evil that befell the boy because he was a liar. It *does* apply to life in general, but does not fully express the truth illustrated by the story. On the other hand, it would be far too specific to say that the theme is "A shepherd boy who lies about wolves attacking his flock will not be believed even when the wolf actually comes." This is not a general truth that can be applied to life outside the fable; in fact, it is very close to being simply a statement of the plot of this particular story. It is clear that such a statement *does* apply to the fable, but it *does not* apply to situations in life that do not involve shepherd boys lying about wolf attacks. Thus, stating a theme involves a sort of balancing act. When you think you have expressed the theme of a work, ask yourself whether it fully expresses the idea the author is trying to convey, but without naming any of the characters or describing in detail any of the events of the story. Notice that the moral at the end of "The Boy Who Cried Wolf" meets these criteria.

Since the theme of a literary work is not usually stated explicitly, as it is in the case of a fable, the reader must discover it in the particulars of the story. These particulars include the depiction of the characters in the work (characterization) and the things that the characters are motivated to do (plot). Of course, this makes theme one of the most important concepts to learn, as it allows you to understand the story as a whole.

A story may have several themes, but as with conflict, there will be one central concept which it presents to its readers. Here are a couple of reliable ways to discover theme.

1. Identify motifs. A motif is a recurring thematic element. It is usually a simple, even single-word concept, such as love, nature, or the struggles of poverty. A motif can also be an object which reappears frequently in a story. By understanding that object's role, the reader can understand some concept within the story. Notice that a motif does not give any insight into life or human nature. It is more a topic than a theme. Still, recognizing a story's motifs can lead to identifying its theme. You must examine the motifs to develop theme statements. What does the story show about these motifs? Look for evidence from the text.
2. Examine the characters. Does the main character learn anything as a result of his experiences? Does the reader learn something? Consider a character's actions and their consequences. Is he rewarded or punished? What does that show about the way he was behaving?

Here are a few points to remember about theme:

- The theme should be specific enough so that it is clearly taken from the story.
- The theme should not be a cliché (a trite and overused statement like "Appearances are deceiving" or "Cheaters never prosper"). This is too general.
- Neither should the theme be a sentence about plot, such as "Mary learned to be patient with her younger sister." This is too specific. Rather, it should be based on the story's specific characters and events, but apply to life outside the story.
- Think of the parables or stories that Jesus told, such as the story of the Good Samaritan. The motif could be "caring for others," but the theme is a longer statement: We must care for those whom we see in need, without any concern about their background.

LESSON 1

"The Discontented Pendulum"
Jane Taylor*

An old clock, that had stood for fifty years in a farmer's kitchen, without giving its owner any cause of complaint, early one summer's morning, before the family was stirring, suddenly stopped.

Upon this, the dial-plate (if we may credit the fable) changed countenance with alarm; the hands made a vain effort to continue their course; the wheels remained motionless with surprise; the weights hung speechless; each member felt disposed to lay the blame on the others. At length the dial instituted a formal inquiry as to the cause of the stagnation, when hands, wheels, weights, with one voice protested their innocence. But now a faint tick was heard below from the pendulum, who spoke thus:

"I confess myself to be the sole cause of the present stoppage; and I am willing, for the general satisfaction, to assign my reasons. The truth is, that I am tired of ticking." Upon hearing this, the old clock became so enraged, that it was on the very point of striking.

"Lazy wire!" exclaimed the dial-plate, holding up its hands.

"Very good!" replied the pendulum; "it is vastly easy for you, Mistress Dial, who have always, as everybody knows, set yourself up above me,—it is vastly easy for you, I say, to accuse other people of laziness! You, who have had nothing to do all the days of your life but to stare people in the face, and to amuse yourself with watching all that goes on in the kitchen! Think, I beseech you, how would you like to be shut up for life in this dark closet, and to wag backwards and forwards, year after year, as I do?

"As to that," said the dial, "is there not a window in your house, on purpose for you to look through?"

"For all that," resumed the pendulum, "it is very dark here; and, although there is a window, I dare not stop, even for an instant, to look out at it. Besides, I am really tired of my way of life; and, if you wish, I'll tell you how I took this disgust at my employment. I happened this morning to be calculating how many times I should have to tick in the course only of the next twenty-four hours; perhaps some of you above there can give me the exact sum."

The minute hand, being quick at figures, presently replied, "Eighty-six thousand four hundred times."

---

*slightly adapted

"Exactly so," replied the pendulum. "Well, I appeal to you all, if the very thought of this was not enough to fatigue anyone; and when I began to [think, to] multiply the strokes of one day by those of months and years, really it is no wonder if I felt discouraged at the prospect; so, after a great deal of reasoning and hesitation, thinks I to myself, I'll stop."

The dial could scarcely keep its countenance during this harangue; but, resuming its gravity, thus replied:

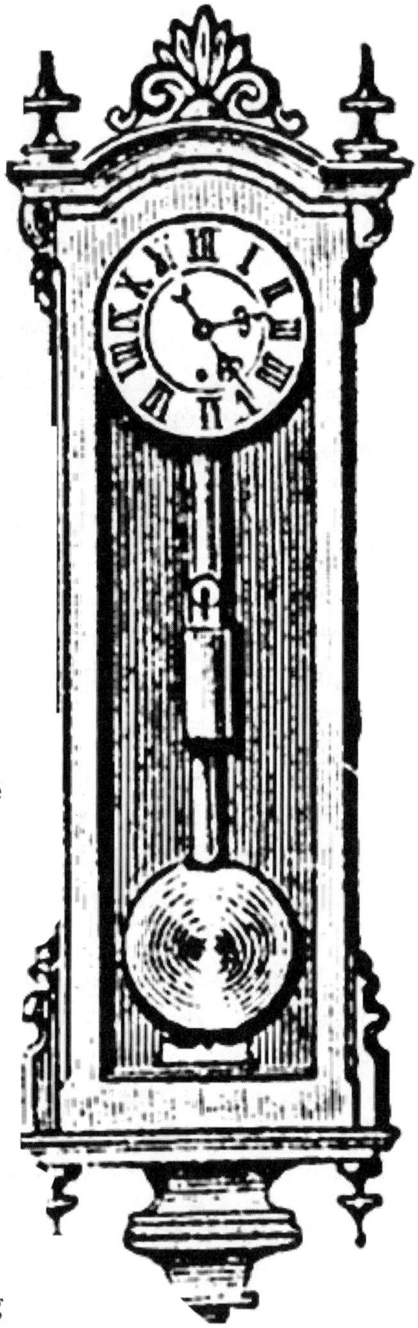

"Dear Mr. Pendulum, I am really astonished that such a useful, industrious person as yourself should have been seized by this sudden weariness. It is true, you have done a great deal of work in your time; so have we all, and are likely to do; which, although it may fatigue us to think of it, the question is whether it will fatigue us to [actually do the work]. Would you now do me the favor to give about half a dozen strokes, to illustrate my argument?"

The pendulum complied, and ticked six times at its usual pace. "Now," resumed the dial, "may I be allowed to inquire, if that exertion was at all fatiguing or disagreeable to you?"

"Not in the least," replied the pendulum; "it is not of six strokes that I complain, nor of sixty, but of millions."

"Very good," replied the dial; "but recollect, that though you may think of a million strokes in an instant, you are required to execute (do) but [only] one [stroke]; and that, however often you may hereafter have to swing, a [full] moment will always be given [to] you to swing in."

"That consideration staggers me, I confess," said the pendulum. "Then I hope," resumed the dial-plate, "we shall all immediately return to our duty; for the maids will lie in bed till noon, if we stand idling thus."

Upon this the weights, who had never been accused of light conduct, used all their influence in urging him to proceed; when, as if with one consent, the wheels began to turn, the hand began to move, the pendulum began to swing, and, to its credit, ticked as loud as ever; while a red beam of the rising sun, that streamed through a hole in the kitchen shutter, shining full upon the dial-plate, it brightened up as if nothing had been the matter.

When the farmer came down to breakfast that morning, upon looking at the clock, he declared that his watch had gained half an hour in the night.

LESSON 1

EXERCISES

Characterization

1. Who are the two main characters in the story? ______________________

____

2. Which one appears to be wiser? ______________________

3. Does the pendulum have a reputation for being lazy or hard-working? How do we know?

____

____

4. At the end of the story, the farmer thinks that his watch must be wrong. What is it about the clock's character that keeps the farmer from suspecting that the clock might be to blame?

____

____

____

Plot

5. Describe in your own words the thought process that led the pendulum to stop swinging.

____

____

____

____

6. In your own words, recount the argument that the dial-plate makes in an effort to convince the pendulum. ______________________

____

____

____

7. This story contains two conflicts. On the one hand, the pendulum quarrels with the other members of the clock, and in particular with the dial (man versus man). On the other hand, the pendulum is struggling with himself when he thinks of all the work he must do (man versus self). Which of these two conflicts gives rise to the other? ______________________________

____

8. What action occurs at the climax of the story? ______________________________

____

____

____

9. What is the resolution? ____

____

____

____

Theme

10. The theme (in this case, the moral) of the fable should be plain, although it may take some effort to express it. In the blank below, compose a theme statement by following the guidelines given in the introduction. ______________________

____

____

____

____

____

St. Joan d'Arc

Mary Lynch

Chapter 1

Because Saint Joan of Arc obeyed God, America is free today. This is how it happened.

In the year of Our Lord 1424, a young girl named Joan d'Arc was kneeling in the soft, sun-warmed grass bordering her father's vegetable garden. She was saying her Rosary and had just finished the Joyful Mysteries.

"Joan!"

The girl glanced quickly toward the big tree growing just beyond the garden. She and her friends called it the "Fairies' tree" and used it as a meeting and play place. Joan thought that her name had been called by one of her friends. She was just going to call out, "Where are you?" in her laughing voice, when she heard her name called again.

"Joan!"

Joan was startled to see nothing but a bright light. The voice was firm, but not unpleasant. It seemed to come from the light. She could see the village church behind the light.

"What do you want? Who are you? Where are you?"

"Joan! Do not fear! I have a message for you from God!" Joan had started to stand up, but at these words she fell back on her knees.

"From God?" Her voice shook.

"Yes—your prayers for France are heard by God!"

Joan shivered. She believed with all her heart that God hears everyone's prayers. Even so, she had not expected her prayers for France to be answered so dramatically. By now, the light was very bright.

"Who are you?" cried Joan.

"I am God's messenger. He wants you to be good and to go to church often."

Joan answered, "I will be good and go to church—I dedicate myself only to God." Then the bright light faded away. Joan remained quiet, but the voice did not speak any more that day.

Joan usually greeted her family with a happy word, so when she entered the house with a serious expression on her face, her mother was surprised.

"Are you feeling well?" she asked, looking closely into Joan's eyes and patting her cheek.

"Oh, yes, Mama, I'm fine," answered Joan, reaching for her apron. "I'll help you get dinner together. Papa will be coming in soon!"

Joan had three older brothers: James was almost eighteen, Peter was sixteen, and John nearly fifteen years old. They were working in the fields with their father. This left Joan and her seven-year-old sister Catherine to help their mother with the evening meal.

Isabelle d'Arc now watched her daughter carefully. She could see Joan's color was good. Her blue eyes were bright and clear as usual. Isabelle just shook her head. "I'll see if her father notices anything!" she said to herself.

Joan was still thinking of the wonderful voice from Heaven. During dinner, her family noticed that she was quiet and subdued. Though she answered their questions pleasantly, she seemed distant.

At bedtime, Joan unwound her long, shiny black braids from around her head. She kept thinking about how the voice had said her prayers for France had been heard by God. For nearly one hundred years, the French had been besieged by the English army, and Joan had been praying since she was a young child that the wars would end so France could be free. Now, though she yearned to hear more from the voice, she wondered, "Who am I that God should send me a message? I am so young—only thirteen—how could I merit this?"

Then she said the Our Father, the Hail Mary, and the Apostles' Creed, just as her mother had taught her. Joan again resolved to dedicate her life to God. She thanked Him for a wonderful family and good friends, then ended her prayers as always with, "Please, dear God, save France!" Though her mattress was filled with rough straw, Joan fell asleep right away. She was strong and healthy. Her cheeks were always rosy and her eyes bright.

Every day, she helped her family by spinning wool and flax for their clothing. Joan dyed her own clothes red, white, and blue— "the colors of our beautiful France!" From crimson berries she picked in the woods, she dyed the wool for her long skirt a bright red. She always wore a white linen blouse with a high neck and sleeves to her elbows. Over the blouse, Joan wore a blue linen bodice which she laced with strands of red wool. She picked tiny blue berries from wild cherry trees to dye her bodice. Every day she braided little bows of red, white, and blue wool into her black hair. Joan knitted long, white wool stockings, which she kept tied above her knees by pulling strands of wool in and out around the top edges and tying them in a bow.

Joan's father and brothers made the family shoes by sewing long, foot-shaped pieces of leather together at the outside edges. The many deer in the woods provided leather for Joan, her mother, and little Catherine. The men's shoes were of specially dried, thick boar's skin.

Jack d'Arc grew flax plants on his farm, and his wife wove linen from the flax. He let the sheep and lambs graze on his fields and sheared their coats for wool. His land also supported some goats and several cows. He had apple and cherry trees, as well as grape vines, from which he made a wonderful white wine.

Jack's greatest pride was his vegetable garden. He grew tomatoes, parsnips, potatoes, strawberries, sweet potatoes, lettuce, onions, and celery; and many herbs, especially sage, chives, various mints, fennel, and dill. It was a living salad!

None of the country families living in Domremy considered themselves rich, yet they wanted for nothing. They loved God and were faithful Catholics. On Sundays and special holy days, they attended Mass. They rested from their labors on those days, except from milking the cows and goats.

The Domremy villagers enjoyed hunting in the nearby woods, and they vied with each other for the biggest fish in the nearby river. There were races and games for prizes on special festival days.

One of Joan's duties was to care for the villagers' animals. The whole village shared this task, and Joan did her family's part. She took the animals into the fields surrounding Domremy, and usually did some mending when she was shepherding.

When Joan was only three, she started helping her mother keep their home clean. Twice a day, Joan swept up all the loose items from the dirt floor. When she finished, she said a prayer of thanks to Our Lord for giving her family such a beautiful home.

Her father had built the house from yellow stones dug out of the surrounding fields and thatched the roof with dried grass. A stork had made a nest near the chimney, which all the country folk claimed was a lucky omen.

Jack had whitewashed the inside walls to make the house seem bright and cheerful. During nice days, light streamed in through the front and back doors and two small windows, one of which overlooked his garden.

The large fireplace at one end of the house served as a kitchen area. There was a big, black iron kettle hanging over the fire in which Isabelle kept a perpetual soup steaming. She added to it frequently—a whole onion, a bunch of thyme, or perhaps a piece of cheese to make it salty. The soup was always ready to be eaten.

In the middle of the house was a large oak table made of thick boards. Jack had smoothed its top and sides, and had made stools to fit around the table for all the members of his family. He made a special high stool with a back and arms for the baby.

At the other end of his house, Jack had built three stalls for sleeping chambers. Baby Catherine slept in Joan's stall, the boys slept in another, and Jack and Isabelle had the largest one.

As soon as Jack had finished building the home, he said, "Now, here is the Head of our house." Then he put over the front door a crucifix he had carved out of dark wood. Isabelle had formed the Corpus out of clay and painted it. She was very artistic. Her husband made a special little shelf under the crucifix, where she kept a bowl of flowers. She also kept pots of flowers on the table and the window sills.

Joan was very devout even as a child because she had the beautiful example of her father and mother. She went to Mass several times a week, often with her mother and sister. Mass was at six o'clock in the morning.

On this night, Joan lay thinking about the heavenly Voice. A messenger from God? What could it mean? Joan shivered a little as she fell asleep.

QUESTIONS

1. List the d'Arc children with their ages. ______________________________

   ____

   ____

2. Underline three examples in the story that show Joan to be a hard worker.

3. What is God's message to Joan? ______________________________

   ____

   ____

LESSON 2

"The Gentle Hand"
T. S. Arthur

I did not hear the maiden's name; but in my thought I have ever since called her "Gentle Hand." What a magic lay in her touch! It was wonderful.

When and where, it matters not now to relate—but once upon a time, as I was passing through a thinly peopled district of country, night came down upon me almost unawares. Being on foot, I could not hope to gain the village toward which my steps were directed, until a late hour; and I therefore preferred seeking shelter and a night's lodging at the first humble dwelling that presented itself.

Dusky twilight was giving place to deeper shadows, when I found myself in the vicinity of a dwelling, from the small uncurtained windows of which the light shone with a pleasant promise of good cheer and comfort. The house stood within an enclosure, and a short distance from the road along which I was moving with wearied feet.

Turning aside, and passing through an ill-hung gate, I approached the dwelling. Slowly the gate swung on its wooden hinges, and the rattle of its latch, in closing, did not disturb the air until I had nearly reached the little porch in front of the house, in which a slender girl, who had noticed my entrance, stood awaiting my arrival.

A deep, quick bark answered, almost like an echo, the sound of the shutting gate, and, sudden as an apparition, the form of an immense dog loomed in the doorway. I was now near enough to see the savage aspect of the animal, and the gathering motion of his body, as he prepared to bound forward upon me. His wolfish growl was really fearful. At the instant when he was about to spring, a light hand was laid upon his shaggy neck, and a low word spoken.

"Don't be afraid. He won't hurt you," said a voice, that to me sounded very sweet and musical.

I now came forward, but in some doubt as to the young girl's power over the beast, on whose rough neck her almost childish hand still lay. The dog did not seem by any means reconciled to my approach, and growled wickedly his dissatisfaction.

"Go in, Tiger," said the girl, not in a voice of authority, yet in her gentle tones was the consciousness that she would be obeyed; and, as she spoke, she lightly bore upon the animal with her hand, and he turned away, and disappeared within the dwelling.

"Who's that?" A rough voice asked the question; and now a heavy-looking man took the dog's place in the door.

"Who are you? What's wanted?" There was something very harsh and forbidding in the way the man spoke. The girl now laid her hand upon his arm, and leaned, with a gentle pressure, against him.

"How far is it to G----?" I asked, not deeming it best to say, in the beginning, that I sought a resting-place for the night.

"To G----!" growled the man, but not so harshly as at first. "It's a good six miles from here."

"A long distance; and I'm a stranger, and on foot," said I. "If you can make room for me until morning, I will be very thankful."

I saw the girl's hand move quickly up his arm, until it rested on his shoulder, and now she leaned to him still closer.

"Come in. We'll try what can be done for you." There was a change in the man's voice that made me wonder. I entered a large room, in which blazed a brisk fire. Before the fire sat two stout lads, who turned upon me their heavy eyes, with no very welcome greeting. A middle-aged woman was standing at a table, and two children were amusing themselves with a kitten on the floor.

"A stranger, mother," said the man who had given me so rude a greeting at the door; "and he wants us to let him stay all night."

The woman looked at me doubtingly for a few moments, and then replied coldly, "We don't keep a public-house."

"I'm aware of that, ma'am," said I; "but night has overtaken me, and it's a long way yet to G----."

"Too far for a tired man to go on foot," said the master of the house, kindly, "so it's no use talking about it, mother; we must give him a bed."

So unobtrusively, that I scarcely noticed the movement, the girl had drawn to the woman's side. What she said to her, I did not hear, for the brief words were uttered in a low voice; but I noticed, as she spoke, one small, fair hand rested on the woman's hand.

Was there magic in that gentle touch? The woman's repulsive aspect changed into one of kindly welcome, and she said, "Yes, it's a long way to G----. I guess we can find a place for him. Have you had any supper?"

I answered in the negative.

The woman, without further remark, drew a pine table from the wall, placed upon it some cold meat, fresh bread and butter, and a pitcher of new milk. While these preparations were going on, I had more leisure for minute observation. There was a singular contrast between the young girl I have mentioned and the other inmates of the room; and yet, I could trace a strong likeness between the maiden and the woman, whom I supposed to be her mother—browned and hard as were the features of the latter.

Soon after I had commenced eating my supper, the two children who were playing on the floor began quarrelling with each other.

"John! Go off to bed!" said the father, in a loud, peremptory voice, speaking to one of the children.

But John, though he could not help hearing, did not choose to obey.

"Do you hear me, sir? Off with you!" repeated the angry father.

"I don't want to go," whined the child.

"Go, I tell you, this minute!"

Still, there was not the slightest movement to obey; and the little fellow looked the very image of rebellion. At this crisis in the affair, when a storm seemed inevitable, the sister, as I supposed her to be, glided across the room, and stooping down, took the child's hands in hers. Not a word was said; but the young rebel was instantly subdued. Rising, he passed out by her side, and I saw no more of him during the evening.

Soon after I had finished my supper, a neighbor came in, and it was not long before he and the man of the house were involved in a warm political discussion, in which were many more assertions than reasons. My host was not a very clear-headed man; while his antagonist was wordy and specious. The former, as might be supposed, very naturally became excited, and, now and then, indulged himself in rather strong expressions toward his neighbor, who, in turn, dealt back wordy blows that were quite as heavy as he had received, and a good deal more irritating.

And now I marked again the power of that maiden's gentle hand. I did not notice her movement to her father's side. She was there when I first observed her, with one hand laid upon his temple, and lightly smoothing the hair with a caressing motion. Gradually the high tone of the disputant subsided, and his words had in them less of personal rancor. Still, the discussion went on; and I noticed that the maiden's hand, which rested on the temple when unimpassioned words were spoken, resumed its caressing motion the instant there was the smallest perceptible tone of anger in the father's voice.

It was a beautiful sight; and I could but look on and wonder at the power of that touch, so light and unobtrusive, yet possessing a spell over the hearts of all around her. As she stood there, she looked like an angel of peace, sent to still the turbulent waters of human passion. Sadly out of place, I could not but think her, amid the rough and rude; and yet, who more than they need the softening and humanizing influences of one like the Gentle Hand.

Many times more, during that evening, did I observe the magic power of her hand and voice—the one gentle yet potent as the other. On the next morning, breakfast being over, I was preparing to take my departure, when my host informed me that if I would wait for half an hour he would give me a ride in his wagon to G----, as business required him to go there. I was very well pleased to accept of the invitation. In due time, the farmer's wagon was driven into the road before the house, and I was invited to get in. I noticed the horse as a rough-looking Canadian pony, with a certain air of stubborn endurance. As the farmer took his seat by my side, the family came to the door to see us off.

"Dick!" said the farmer, in a peremptory voice, giving the rein a quick jerk as he spoke.

But Dick moved not a step.

"Dick! You vagabond! Get up." And the farmer's whip cracked sharply by the pony's ear.

It availed not, however, this second appeal. Dick stood firmly disobedient. Next the whip was brought down upon him, with an impatient hand; but the pony only reared up a little. Fast and sharp the strokes were next dealt to the number of half a dozen. The man might as well have beaten his wagon, for all his end was gained.

A stout lad now came out into the road, and catching Dick by the bridle, jerked him forward, using, at the same time, the customary language on such occasions, but Dick met this new ally with increased stubbornness, planting his forefeet more firmly, and at a sharper angle with the ground. The impatient boy now struck the pony on the side of his head with his clenched hand, and jerked cruelly at his bridle. It availed nothing, however; Dick was not to be wrought upon by any such arguments.

"Don't do so, John!" I turned my head as the maiden's sweet voice reached my ear. She was passing through the gate into the road, and in the next moment had taken hold of the lad and drawn him away from the animal. No strength was exerted in this; she took hold of his arm, and he obeyed her wish as readily as if he had no thought beyond her gratification.

And now that soft hand was laid gently on the pony's neck, and a single low word spoken. How instantly were the tense muscles relaxed—how quickly the stubborn air vanished!

"Poor Dick!" said the maiden, as she stroked his neck lightly, or softly patted it with a child-like hand. "Now, go along, you provoking fellow!" she added, in a half-chiding, yet affectionate voice, as she drew upon the bridle.

The pony turned toward her, and rubbed his head against her arm for an instant or two; then, pricking up his ears, he started off at a light, cheerful trot, and went on his way as freely as if no silly crotchet had ever entered his stubborn brain.

"What a wonderful power that hand possesses!" said I, speaking to my companion, as we rode away.

He looked at me for a moment as if my remark had occasioned surprise. Then a light came into his countenance, and he said, briefly, "She's good! Everybody and everything loves her."

Was that, indeed, the secret of her power? Was the quality of her soul perceived in the impression of her hand, even by brute beasts! The father's explanation was, doubtless, the true one. Yet have I ever since wondered, and still do wonder, at the potency which lay in that maiden's magic touch. I have seen something of the same power, showing itself in the loving and the good, but never to the extent as instanced in her, whom, for a better name, I must still call "Gentle Hand."

A gentle touch, a soft word. Ah! How few of us, when the will is strong with its purpose, can believe in the power of agencies so apparently insignificant! And yet all great influences effect their ends silently, unobtrusively, and with a force that seems at first glance to be altogether inadequate. Is there not a lesson for us all in this?

LESSON 2

EXERCISES

Characterization

1. Describe the character of "Gentle Hand." Take into account what she does and the things that others say about her. ______________________________

____

____

2. Come up with two adjectives or phrases to describe the flawed character of the narrator's host. Think about the way he greets the narrator at his house, the way he reacts to his son's refusal to go to bed, the political discussion he has with his neighbor, and the way he treats his stubborn pony. Try to be specific in your answer; don't just say that he is "bad" or "mean."

____

____

3. Name two other human characters in the story on whom "Gentle Hand" has a marvelous effect. What character flaw(s) does she help each to overcome?

   a. ______________________________

   ____

   b. ______________________________

   ____

4. The windows of the house are "uncurtained" and the gate is "ill-hung." What do these details suggest about the people who live there? ______________________________

____

____

____

Plot

5. Why do you think that the man of the house and the middle-aged woman are reluctant at first to let the narrator spend the night? ______________________

____

____

6. When the man and his son engage in a battle of wills over bedtime, what category of conflict does this illustrate? ______________________

____

7. When the man and his neighbor are engaged in their political discussion, "Gentle Hand" helps the man to control his anger. Into which category of conflict would you place his struggle with his anger? ______________________

____

8. Into what category of conflict (see p. ix) would you place the man's attempt to motivate his horse?

____

____

9. Notice that the plot of this story consists in a series of conflicts that are resolved through the actions and words of "Gentle Hand." Which of the Beatitudes does this remind you of?

____

____

Theme

10. Choose the statement that best expresses the theme of this story, and put a check by it. Label the other statements as too specific, too general, or beside the point.

a. ______________ Gentleness is a beautiful quality.

b. ______________ A gentle woman can tame the hearts of men and beasts with the mere touch of her hand.

c. ______________ Gentle persuasion often removes obstacles that could never be conquered by direct confrontation.

d. ______________ One should avoid discussing politics with one's neighbors.

St. Joan d'Arc

Mary Lynch

Chapter 2

The next morning, it was Joan's turn to take the town animals out to pasture. The d'Arc family had five cows, a nanny and a billy goat, six sheep, and a horse. Joan quickly milked the cows and the goat and gathered them together with the sheep. By the time she had finished, the neighbors had brought their animals for Joan to shepherd out to the fields. She had charge of nine cows, sixteen sheep, three goats, and two horses.

It was a sunny and blue morning, with fluffy clouds lazily floating across the sky. Joan urged all the animals before her into the open countryside. She had some trouble keeping the cows away from a stand of golden and green corn at the end of the property, so she called to her dog Beau, a beautiful Shetland sheep dog.

Beau nipped at the cows' heels until they followed Joan. As they walked along, Joan called the animals by name and talked with them. She had filled her big skirt pocket with seeds for the birds, a crust of bread to nibble on herself, and a special bone for Beau.

When they arrived at a sunny meadow, the best spot for the animals to find tasty clover, Joan sat down on a large, flat gray stone. She gave the bone to Beau and sprinkled the seeds on the ground. Pretty soon, some noisy sparrows, two mockingbirds, a robin, and a family of pigeons came fluttering to the seeds. Joan spoke softly to them:

"Ah—you sweet little birds of God! Are you hungry? I hope you like your breakfast!" The seeds disappeared quickly, so Joan broke up her crust for the birds. Beau would have chased them away, but she said,

"Beau, they are eating peacefully. You mustn't disturb them!" So he laid down next to Joan, his head on his paws, tail wagging from side to side, and eyes twitching from one bird to the other. He did not move until Joan told him to fetch a stray lamb back to its mother. He was a good dog.

Joan did not try to say her Rosary while she was in charge of the animals—she had to keep track of them, or they might wander into trouble. As she sat, though, she wondered about the wonderful Voice and the bright light. Would she ever hear the Voice or see the light again? She was anxious and eager at the same time. Finally, the sun was high in the sky; it was time to return home with her flock.

Joan's mother had the noon meal ready for her family, but Joan was missing.

"Well, Madame d'Arc, and where is Joan?" Jack pulled a stool from the table to sit down.

He was proud of his whole family and adored his beautiful wife, Isabelle. She had wavy black hair, brown eyes, and creamy pink skin. Jack had curly blond hair and blue eyes with fair skin. His children were obedient, respectful, and full of joy. They loved to play with the other village children and to celebrate the holy Feast Days of the Catholic Church. Jack considered the noon meal to be the family's best time together.

Now Isabelle answered her husband, "She said she wanted to check on something in your garden."

"Oh! Well, alright," said Jack. Isabelle knew the garden was her husband's treasure, so if Joan was taking care of something there, that was fine with him.

In the garden, Joan was kneeling and saying her Rosary, as on the day before. This day being Tuesday, she was starting the Sorrowful Mysteries. She heard her name called again.

"Joan—Joan!" said the Voice. Joan couldn't help trembling with anxiety.

"Joan, do not be afraid! I have come from God to tell you to be good and to go to church." A bright light again accompanied these words, but today Joan felt that she was surrounded by it. She wanted to answer the Voice, but was not sure what to say, so she repeated her words from Monday:

"I will be good; I will go to church; I will give myself to God!"

Then, as yesterday, the light disappeared, and Joan heard the Voice no more. She was still trembling, but was not as frightened as before. In fact, Joan admitted to herself that the Voice was comforting. Besides, the Voice said he came from God. Joan felt a thrill of joy.

Just as she finished the Rosary, she noticed some weeds among the lettuce. After she pulled them out, she saw some among the tomatoes and pulled them out as well. When Joan went back into the house, her family was just finishing their meal.

Her father said, "Well, Joan! What did you do in my garden?"

Joan answered, "I found some weeds among your lettuce and tomatoes, so I pulled them out." She smiled at her father.

"Ah-h-h! Thank you, Joan! Did you notice if the tomatoes are ripe yet?"

"They are still rather green, and one looked as if something had taken a bite out of it!" Joan's father became so distracted about his vegetables that he did not notice Joan's serious demeanor. Her mother did notice.

The next morning, Joan awoke and went about her chores. She appeared calm, but was agitated inside. She was too humble to say anything about the Voice, even to her mother, but questions were tumbling through her mind. Had she imagined it? Was it truly from God? Why was she, a simple country girl, hearing a heavenly Voice? She could hardly wait until noontime, when she could return to her father's garden. Would she hear the Voice again?

Isabelle saw how quiet Joan had become during the last few days, but she had learned long ago that it was best to wait for an answer rather than to start questioning.

Joan finished her morning chores and began churning the butter to prepare for market. It was a major source of her family's income.

At the noon hour, Joan walked carefully to the garden, knelt down, and took her Rosary from the pocket of her red skirt. She realized she must make another repair in the pocket. She always had something going in and out of that pocket—bread for the birds, a straw ball for her little sister, or an unusual stone for the tiny altar by her bed. Joan had a very busy pocket.

It was Wednesday; so Joan finished the Glorious Mysteries. She always ended her Rosary with the "Hail! Holy Queen" and the prayer to St. Michael the Archangel.

"Do thou, O Prince of the heavenly Host by the power of God, thrust into Hell Satan and the other evil spirits who wander about the world seeking the ruin of souls. Pray for us, O Holy Mother of God, that we may be worthy of the promises of Christ."

A great light suddenly surrounded Joan. It was as bright as the sun, yet did not hurt her eyes. Out of this brilliance appeared a thrilling sight: a beautiful young man with brown hair flowing to his shoulders. He wore a dazzling jeweled golden crown and a white robe cinctured about his waist by a belt of gold. He held out his hand toward Joan as in blessing and said with a kind smile:

"Do not fear, Joan. You are cherished by God who has great blessings for you!"

Joan wanted to ask this lovely, heavenly person who he was, but she could not make a sound. In answer to her thoughts came the words:

"I am Michael, Archangel of God, and Prince of the Heavenly Host!" His voice was pleasant and soothing to Joan. She was not afraid. Still, she wondered why such a great angel should come to her.

Suddenly, Michael was surrounded by many other angels. All wore golden crowns and were glorious in their white and gold robes. Their beautiful faces were filled with smiles of love and tenderness.

Michael the Archangel spoke again: "Joan, Daughter of France, be a good girl and obey God's laws." Joan was almost paralyzed with love at the marvelous sight. With the Archangel's last words, all the angels vanished.

Joan sank slowly to the ground, unable even to kneel any longer. Her shaking knees could not support her trembling body. She was still half kneeling, half sitting among the vegetables a few minutes later when she heard her mother's voice calling her.

Joan could hardly speak, but she managed a husky, "Yes, Mother?"

Noticing the strange tone of Joan's voice, her mother went out to her.

"What is the matter, Joan?" she asked, concerned at Joan's dazed expression. She thought, "She can't be catching cold—it's the middle of summer! What could be the problem?"

Isabelle gently guided Joan back to the house. "I'll let her tell me about it in her own good time!" she said to herself.

QUESTIONS

1. What do the contents of Joan's pocket show about her character? Name at least one characteristic. ______________________________
____
____

2. How does Joan respond to the appearance of the angels? ______________________________
____
____

3. Who notices that Joan is acting differently than usual? ______________________________
____

LESSON 3

"The Czar and the Angel"
Author Unknown

Somewhere, nowhere, in a certain empire, time out of mind, and in no land of ours, dwelt a Czar who was so very proud that he feared neither God nor man. He listened to no good counsel, but did only that which was good in his own eyes, and no one dared to put him right. And all his ministers and nobles grieved exceedingly, and all the people grieved likewise.

One day the Czar went to church and he listened to the priest who was reading from the Scriptures. Now there were certain words in the Holy Book which pleased not the Czar. "Why say such words to me?" thought he, "words that I can never forget, though I grow gray-headed." After service the Czar went home and bade his servants send the priest to him. The priest came.

"How darest thou to read such words to me?" asked the Czar.

"They were written to be read," replied the priest.

"Written, indeed! And wouldst thou then read everything that is written? Blot out those words and never dare to read them again, I command thee!"

"It is not I who have written the words of the Holy Scripture, your Majesty," said the priest; "nor is it for me to blot them out."

"What! Thou dost presume to teach me? I am the Czar, and it is thy duty to obey me."

"In all things will I obey thee, O Czar, save only in sacred things. God is over them; men cannot alter them," answered the priest.

"Not alter them!" roared the Czar. "If I wish them altered, altered they must be. Strike me out those words instantly, I say, and never dare read them in church again. Dost thou hear?"

"I dare not," said the priest. "I have no will in the matter."

"I command thee, fellow!"

"I dare not, O Czar!"

"Well," said the Czar, "I'll give thee three days to think about it. On the evening of the fourth day appear before me, and I'll strike thy head from thy shoulders if thou dost not obey me!"

Then the priest bowed low and returned to his home.

The third day was already drawing to a close and the priest knew not what to do. It was no great terror to him to die for the faith, but what would become of his wife and children? He walked about, and wept, and wrung his hands:

"Oh, woe is me! Woe is me!"

At last he lay down on his bed, but not until dawn did he close his eyes in sleep. Then he saw in a dream an Angel standing at his head.

"Fear nothing!" said the Angel. "God hath sent me down on earth to protect thee!"

So, early in the morning, the priest rose up full of joy and prayed gratefully to God.

The Czar also awoke early in the morning and shouted to his huntsmen to gather together and go hunting with him in the forest.

So away they went to the hunt, and it was not long before a stag leaped out of the thicket beneath the very eyes of the Czar. He galloped after it. Every moment the stag seemed to be faltering, and yet the Czar could never quite come up with it. Eager with excitement, he spurred on his horse.

"Faster, faster!" he cried; "now we have him!"

But here a stream crossed the road, and the stag plunged into the water. The Czar was a good swimmer. "Surely I shall take him now," thought he. "A little longer, and I shall hold him by the horns."

So the Czar took off his clothes, and into the water he plunged after the stag. The stag swam across to the opposite bank, but just as the Czar was extending his hand to seize him by the horns, there was no longer any stag to be seen. It was the Angel who had taken the form of a stag. The Czar was amazed. He looked about him on every side and wondered where the stag had gone.

At that moment he saw someone on the other side of the river, putting on the Czar's royal clothes, and presently he mounted the Czar's own horse and galloped away. The Czar thought it was some evildoer, but it was the selfsame Angel, who had now gone away to collect the huntsmen and take them home. As for the Czar, he remained all naked and solitary in the forest.

At last he looked about him and saw, far, far away, smoke rising above the forest, and something like a dark cloud standing in the clear sky.

"Perhaps," said he to himself, "that smoke is from my hunting pavilion."

So he went in the direction of the smoke and came at last to a brick kiln. The brick burners came forth to meet him and were amazed to see a man without clothing. They saw that his feet were lame and bruised, and his body covered with scratches.

"Give me to drink," said he, "and I would fain eat something also."

The brick burners had pity on him; they gave him an old tattered garment to wear and a piece of black bread to eat. Never from the day of his birth had the Czar had such a tasty meal.

"And now speak, O man!" said they; "Who art thou?"

"I'll tell you who I am," said he, when he had eaten his fill; "I am your Czar. Lead me to my capital, and there I will reward you!"

"What, thou wretched rogue!" they cried. "Thou dost presume to mock us, thou old ragamuffin, and magnify thyself into a Czar! Thou reward us, indeed!"

And they looked at him in amazement and scorn.

"Dare to laugh at me again," said he, "and I'll have your heads chopped off!"

For he forgot himself and thought he was at home.

"What! Thou!" shouted the brick burners, and they fell upon him, and beat him most unmercifully, and then they drove away, and off he went, groaning, into the forest.

He went on and on till at last he saw once more a smoke rising up out of the wood. Again he thought:

"That is surely from my hunting pavilion," and so he went up to it.

And behold, he had come to another brick kiln. There, too, they had pity upon and kindly treated him. They gave him to eat and to drink. They also gave him ragged hose and a tattered shirt, for they were very poor people. They took him to be a runaway soldier or some other poor man; but when he had eaten his fill and clothed himself, he said to them:

"I am your Czar!"

They laughed at him, and again he began to talk roughly to the people. Then they fell upon him, and thrashed him soundly, and drove him away. And he wandered all by himself through the forest till it was night. Then he laid himself down beneath a tree and slept until the morning, when he continued his journey.

At last he came to a third brick kiln, but he did not tell the brick burners there that he was the czar. All he thought of now was how he might reach his capital. These people, too, treated him kindly, and seeing that his feet were lame and bruised, they had compassion upon him and gave him a pair of very old boots. And he asked them:

"Do ye know by which way I can get to the capital?"

They told him; but it was a long, long road and a weary journey.

But he followed the road which they had pointed out. He went on and on till he came to a little town, and there the roadside sentries stopped him.

"Halt!" they cried.

He halted.

"Whence art thou?" asked the soldiers.

"I am going to the capital," answered the Czar.

"Thou art a vagabond!" they cried.

So they took him to the capital and put him in a dungeon. After a time the custodians came round to examine the prisoner.

"Who art thou, old man?" they asked. Then he told them the whole truth.

"Once I was the Czar," said he, and he related all that had befallen him. They were amazed, for he was not at all like a Czar. For indeed he had been growing thin and haggard for a long time, and his beard was all long and tangled. And yet, for all that, he insisted that he was the Czar. So they made up their minds that he was crazy and drove him away.

"Why should we keep this fool forever," said they, "and waste the Czar's bread upon him?"

Never did any man feel so wretched on God's earth as did that wretched Czar. Willingly would he have done any sort of work if he had only known how, but he had never been used to work and therefore was obliged to beg his bread, and could scarce beg enough to keep body and soul together. He lay at night at the first place that came to hand, sometimes in the tall grass, sometimes beneath a fence.

"Who could have thought that it should ever come to this!" he sighed.

Now the Angel, who had made himself Czar, had gone home with the huntsmen. And no man knew that he was not a Czar but an Angel. The same evening the priest came to him and said:

"Do thy will, O Czar, and strike off my head, for I cannot blot out one word of Holy Scripture."

And the Czar said to him:

"Glory be to God, for now I know that there is at least one priest in my land who stands firm for God's Word. I'll make thee the highest bishop in this realm."

The priest thanked him, bowed down to the earth, and departed, marveling.

"What is this wonder," thought he, "that the haughty Czar should have become so just and gentle?"

But all men marveled at the change that had come over the ruler. He was now mild and gracious; no longer did he spend all his days in the forest, but went about inquiring of his people if any were wronged or injured by their neighbors and if justice were done. He took count of all, and rebuked the unjust judges, and saw that every man had his rights. And the people now rejoiced as much as they had grieved heretofore, and justice was done in all the courts, and no bribes were taken. But the Czar, the real Czar, grew more and more wretched.

Then, after three years, an order went forth from the palace that all the people were to come together to a great banquet given by the Czar; all were to be there, both rich and poor, both high and lowly. And all the people came, and the unhappy Czar came, too. And so many long tables were set out in the Czar's courtyard that all the people praised God when they saw the glad sight.

They all sat down at table and ate and drank, and the Angel Czar himself and his courtiers distributed the meat and drink to the guests as much as they would, but to the unfortunate Czar they gave a double portion of everything. When all had eaten and drunk their fill, the Angel Czar that ruled over the land began to inquire whether any had suffered injustice or wrong. And when the people began to disperse, the Czar stood at the gate and gave to everyone a piece of money.

And again, after three years, he made yet another banquet and proclaimed that all should come, both rich and poor. And all the people came and ate and drank and bowed low before the Angel Czar and thanked him and made ready to depart. The unfortunate Czar was also on the point of going, when the Angel Czar stopped him, and took him aside into the palace, and said to him:

"Lo! God hath tried thee and chastised thy pride these many years. But me He sent to teach thee that a Czar must have regard to the complaints of his people. So thou wast made poor and a vagabond that thou mightest pick up wisdom, if but a little. Look now, that thou doest good to thy people and judgest righteous judgment, as now thou shalt be Czar again, but I must return to Heaven." And when the Angel had said this, he was no more to be seen.

Then the Czar prayed gratefully to God, and from henceforth he ruled his people justly, as the Angel had bidden him.

LESSON 3

EXERCISES

Characterization

1. What is a czar? Use a dictionary if necessary. ______________________________

____

____

2. Look carefully at the czar's actions at the beginning of the story. Can you think of another adjective to describe the czar besides proud? ______________________________

____

3. How does the character of the priest contrast with that of the czar? Give concrete examples of their actions that illustrate the difference in their characters. ______________________________

____

____

____

____

4. Based on what you have learned about characterization, why do you think that the people are amazed at the change that has apparently come over the czar? ______________________________

____

____

____

5. Contrast the character of the czar with the Angel Czar. Give concrete examples of their actions that illustrate the difference in their characters. ______________________________

____

____

____

____

Plot

6. In which country do you think this story takes place? ______

7. Why does the czar become angry with the priest? ______

8. What does the czar command the priest to do? ______

9. Does the priest obey? ______

10. Although the priest is willing to die for his faith, what thought causes him great anxiety?

11. After the Angel appears to the priest in a dream, how does his attitude show his trust in God?

12. When the czar visits the first two brick kilns, how do the brick burners treat him at first?

13. How would you characterize the actions and words of the czar that make the brick burners beat him and drive him off? ______

14. Why do the brick burners not believe that he is the czar? ______

15. By the time he comes to the third brick kiln, what lesson has the czar learned? ______

16. After the czar is arrested by his own soldiers, the custodians of the prison come around to examine him. According to the story, why do they not believe that he is really the czar?

___

___

17. After he is ejected from his own dungeon, what is the czar forced to do in order to survive?

___

___

18. What happens to the priest, and why? ___

___

___

19. Jesus said "Many that are first shall be last; and the last shall be first" (Matthew 19:30). How does this apply to the changes in fortune experienced by the czar and the priest?

___

___

___

20. In both cases, who was the agent who brought these things about? ___

___

21. Immediately after the Angel becomes the Czar, he does some things that make others marvel at the supposed change in the czar's character. What does he do? ___

___

___

___

22. How many years elapse before the Angel Czar holds his first banquet for the people?

___

23. Look at the actions of the Angel Czar at the banquet, and find one example each of humility, justice, and generosity. ____

____

____

____

24. How many years elapse before the Angel Czar holds a second banquet for the people?

____

25. At the climax of the story, what explanation does the Angel Czar give to the czar for the way he has been treated? ____

____

26. How would you classify the main conflict in this story? Think about the change that has taken place by the time the story reaches its climax. ____

____

____

Theme

27. Look up I Peter Chapter 5 in your Bible. Pick out the sentence in this chapter that is the *best* statement of the theme of this story. Write it in the space below, and then explain your decision.

____

____

____

____

____

____

____

____

St. Joan d'Arc

Mary Lynch

Chapter 3

For Joan, the next three years were the nearest thing to Heaven itself. Every day, she followed her duties at home, joined in games and amusements with her friends from the village, and continued her daily prayers and saying her Rosary.

She went to early morning Mass as often as she could spare time from her duties. For the first time, she began to receive Our Lord in Holy Communion on a regular basis. At that time, Holy Mother Church did not allow anyone to receive Our Lord until he was twelve years of age, because younger children might not understand they were receiving the actual Body and Blood of Our Lord Jesus.

Receiving Our Lord nearly every day was Joan's greatest joy; but, besides this were the times that Saint Michael the Archangel appeared to her. He was often joined by two other saints—Catherine of Alexandria and Margaret of Antioch. Both had been martyred while young girls, during the last days of the persecution of Christians.

St. Catherine of Alexandria's father was an Egyptian king. She gave up her royal rights and privileges to become Christian. After suffering great physical and mental torture, St. Catherine was executed for refusing to give up Our Lord.

St. Margaret's father had been a heathen priest in Antioch, which was the capital of Syria, on the coast of the Mediterranean Sea. Margaret learned about Jesus Christ and the Christian Faith through her nurse, and she converted to Christianity before it had been forbidden by the Roman Emperors. Later, when Christians were persecuted horribly, Margaret's love of Our Lord was so great that she endured much suffering without denying the Faith.

The stories of these saints had been told in Europe by Christians returning from their travels to the Holy Land. They had filled the minds of Europeans for about thirteen centuries when Joan's mother told them to her children. So, when these young saints spoke to Joan and identified themselves, she recognized them immediately.

Although Joan was able to see St. Michael, Sts. Catherine and Margaret never appeared to her. She only heard their voices, and they told her that God chose them to prepare her for a very special mission for the world.

One day when Joan was about ten, her father said, "Come! We are all going to the Fair in Vaucouleurs!" (pronounced Voh-koo-ler).

Vaucouleurs was a few miles from Joan's home in Domremy. It took over an hour for the family to travel there. They were pulled in their small cart by their donkey. Joan's young sister Catherine wanted to ride him, but her mother said,

"It's a hot day today, and it would strain our donkey if you ride him. Sit with me, and we can count all the little birds we see on our way." Little Catherine liked to play with her mother, so she sat happily with her in the cart.

"Why is there a festival today?" asked Peter.

"It is the Feast of the Ascension of Our Lord—today we celebrate Our Lord returning to Heaven."

People from all the surrounding villages were traveling to the festival. Joan said, "Look at all the carts and people going to the Fair!" It was an exciting adventure.

First, everyone attended Mass in the great cathedral. Jack d'Arc tied his donkey to a nearby tree. He and his little family followed the crowd. On the way, a juggler in a red, white, and blue clown costume, his face painted white, tossed five rings around them, narrowly missing John. He laughed with excitement.

Then three acrobats threw themselves all around the family, finally leaping on each other's shoulders. Peter said, "They must be really strong!"

"And crazy, too!" said Jim. "Suppose one of them missed!" All the family laughed.

When they went into Mass, the cathedral was already filled with people, and the crowd pressed on them from every side. So Jack picked Joan up, and Isabelle put Catherine into John's arms. Now Joan could see over the heads of the worshippers. In those days, there were no seats or kneelers in the churches for the congregation, so when Joan was standing on the floor, she could see only the backs of people at her eye level. Everyone was quiet in the cathedral because they were in the Presence of the Lord Jesus Christ, high over the altar in a golden tabernacle.

Joan was perched on her papa's shoulder. When she looked at the great altar, she saw something that was new to her. She pointed at it and whispered, "What is that big red thing on the altar?"

"That's a book," whispered her father. "It is called a Sacramentary. It has all the prayers of the Mass in it." He added, "Here come the priests now! We must all be quiet. Mass is starting!" Then everyone crossed themselves to begin Mass.

Ten altar boys carrying tall lighted candles in big golden candleholders entered the sanctuary first. Then three priests entered. They wore shiny gold vestments with beautiful white lace showing below. The first priest carried a large, golden pear-shaped container with holes in the top, called a censer. A sweet-smelling smoke came out of it as he swung it back and forth by a gold chain. The second priest carried a big red book, which he laid on the altar and opened. The third priest wore a red cassock and a red beretta with a pompom on top.

"That's the bishop!" Jack whispered to Joan. Then all the priests knelt in front of the altar. Everybody in the Church knelt, too. Joan knelt down at first, but the stone floor was hard and cold. Finally, she stood up and leaned against her father. She could see the altar better that way, too.

"Why are there two other priests on the altar?" asked Joan.

"Because it is High Mass! Sh-h-h! I'll tell you about it tonight," answered her father.

Then Joan heard a heavenly sound of music. She turned around to see who was singing. High on a balcony at the back of the Church was a crowd of what looked like angels dressed in white, all singing a hymn to God. As Joan kept looking, she realized the beautiful sounds were the voices of nearly fifty young boys.

When the priest went up to the pulpit to preach, he quoted Our Lord's words at His Ascension into Heaven: "Behold, I am with you always!" Joan knew exactly what Our Lord meant.

After Mass, everyone had fun visiting with people from other villages. They sauntered from one display to the other, laughing and smiling with everybody, even though they had not met before. This was not surprising, since nearly all had just received Our Lord in Holy Communion. Their hearts were joyful.

The sights and sounds of the fair were something to remember. There were so many carts with different and colorful things for sale. Vegetables and fruits of all kinds were piled high—green, red and yellow peppers; orange carrots; yellow and red tomatoes; shiny, rich purple eggplants; red, green and yellow polished apples; and bright red and yellow cherries. Jack d'Arc bought a big sack of these cherries at the insistence of his children, especially Catherine. Catherine could be pretty noisy in order to get her way.

Then there were toys of all colors. There were balls of straw, leather and wood; dolls carved of wood with moving legs and arms, and heads with hair of horse-hair; little wagons painted red and blue; funny little wooden dolls that jumped when you pulled a string.

The ladies admired the beautiful silks, which had been carried all the way from China by Marco Polo. There were colored leather boots for the men; jaunty leather caps with long blue and red feathers on one side; leather hunting gloves for falconing; huge bows and arrows for deer hunting. Joan's brothers lingered longingly over these things.

Little Catherine was in her mother's arms. She started squealing when the d'Arcs came by the animals. There were all kinds, each trying to outdo the others with its noise. They could hear pigs oinking and monkeys chattering. Dogs barked deep woofs or piercing yips, calves cried "mah-mah!" for their mothers, and sheep bahed behind their shepherdess. Chickens clucking, donkeys braying, everything that could make a noise did.

There was music at the fair, too. A man in blue and white tights and a red and yellow jacket played some cheery notes on a flute; another man in red tights and a striped blue and white jacket played teary notes on a lute. There was another short fat man in a clown costume of green and white dots and a painted face; he had a big drum flowing with green and white ribbons, making big boom-booms to the lute and flute notes.

People called out to each other, vendors shouted their prices, and babies cried. But above all the noise, the cathedral bells rang out the joy of Our Lord's Ascension into Heaven. It was a wonderful clamor. Everyone was filled with the gladness of it all.

While the bells were ringing, a gentleman on a beautiful black horse made his way down the street. He was dressed in black and gold, and his horse was caparisoned in black and gold. The man nodded and waved gently as he passed through the crowd, acknowledging their bows and cheers with a pleasant smile. This gentleman was the Lord of the Manor, Sir Robert of Baudricourt. The land that all the villagers lived on was owned by him.

Joan, sitting on her father's shoulders, caught Sir Robert's eye. He blew her a kiss. Joan laughed and blew him a kiss. Little did either of them know that just a short six years later, Sir Robert would help Joan save France. After comments about how pleasant Robert of Baudricourt was, Jack d'Arc and his family continued walking among the Fair's displays.

Joan had many questions to ask her parents that night. Why were there ten altar boys? Why were there so many tall candles? Why? Why? Her mother and father answered all her questions.

QUESTIONS

1. What is the reason for the festival in Vaucouleurs? ____________________

____

2. Why do all the peasants show their respect to Sir Robert of Beaudricourt? ____________

____

____

LESSON 4

"The Last Class—The Story of a Little Alsatian"
Alphonse Daudet

This story takes place at the end of the Franco-Prussian war (1870-71). Alsace, a region between France and Germany, had been claimed by the French, but as the story opens, it has fallen into the hands of Germany (Prussia). As you read, look for evidence that the characters have experienced a change of outlook. How have they changed in their perception of what is valuable? What events have caused this change?

I was late to school that morning, and I was terribly afraid of being scolded, especially as Monsieur Hamel had told us that he should examine us on participles, and I did not know the first thing about them. For a moment I thought of staying away from school and wandering about the fields. It was such a warm, lovely day. I could hear the blackbirds whistling on the edge of the wood, and in the Rippert field, behind the sawmill, the Prussians going through their drill. All that was much more tempting to me than the rules concerning participles; but I had the strength to resist, and I ran as fast as I could to school.

As I passed the mayor's office, I saw that there were people gathered about the little board on which notices were posted. For two years all our bad news had come from that board—battles lost, conscriptions, orders from headquarters; and I thought without stopping:

"What can it be now?"

Then, as I ran across the square, Watcher the blacksmith, who stood there with his apprentice, reading the placard, called out to me: "Don't hurry so, my boy; you'll get to your school soon enough!"

I thought that he was making fun of me, and I ran into Monsieur Hamel's little yard all out of breath. Usually, at the beginning of school, there was a great uproar which could be heard in the street, desks opening and closing, lessons repeated aloud in unison, with our ears stuffed in order to learn quicker, and the teacher's stout ruler beating on the desk:

"A little more quiet!"

I counted on all this noise to reach my bench unnoticed; but as it happened, that day everything was quiet, like a Sunday morning. Through the open window I saw my comrades already in their places, and Monsieur Hamel walking back and forth with the terrible iron ruler under his arm. I had to open the door and enter, in the midst of that perfect silence. You can imagine whether I blushed and whether I was afraid!

But no! Monsieur Hamel looked at me with no sign of anger and said very gently: "Go at once to your seat, my little Frantz; we were going to begin without you."

I stepped over the bench and sat down at once at my desk. Not until then, when I had partly recovered from my fright, did I notice that our teacher had on his handsome blue coat, his plaited ruff, and the black silk embroidered breeches, which he wore only on days of inspection or of distribution of prizes. Moreover, there was something extraordinary, something solemn about the whole class. But what surprised me most was to see at the back of the room, on the benches which were usually empty, some people from the village sitting, as silent as we were: old Hauser with his three-cornered hat, the ex-mayor, the ex-postman, and others besides. They all seemed depressed; and Hauser had brought an old spelling book with gnawed edges, which he held wide open on his knee, with his great spectacles askew.

While I was wondering at all this, Monsieur Hamel had mounted his platform, and in the gentle and serious voice with which he had welcomed me, he said to us:

"My children, this is the last time that I shall teach you. Orders have come from Berlin to teach nothing but German in the schools of Alsace and Lorraine. The new teacher arrives tomorrow. This is the last class in French, so I beg you to be very attentive." Those few words overwhelmed me. Ah! The villains! That was what they had posted at the mayor's office.

My last class in French!

And I barely knew how to write! So I should never learn! I must stop short where I was! How angry I was with myself because of the time I had wasted, the lessons I had missed, running about after nests, or sliding on the Saar! My books, which only a moment before I thought so tiresome, so heavy to carry—my grammar, my sacred history—seemed to me now like old friends, from whom I should be terribly grieved to part. And it was the same about Monsieur Hamel. The thought that he was going away, that I should never see him again, made me forget the punishments, the blows with the ruler.

Poor man! It was in honor of that last lesson that he had put on his fine Sunday clothes; and I understood now why those old fellows from the village were sitting at the end of the room. It seemed to mean that they regretted not having come oftener to the school. It was also a way of thanking our teacher for his forty years of faithful service, and of paying their respects to the fatherland which was vanishing.

I was at that point in my reflections, when I heard my name called. It was my turn to recite. What would I not have given to be able to say from beginning to end that famous rule about participles, in a loud, distinct voice, without a slip! But I got mixed up at the first words, and I stood there swaying against my bench, with a full heart, afraid to raise my head. I heard Monsieur Hamel speaking to me:

"I will not scold you, my little Frantz; you must be punished enough; that is the way it goes; every day we say to ourselves: 'Pshaw! I have time enough. I will learn tomorrow.' And then you see what happens. Ah! It has been the great misfortune of our Alsace always to postpone its lessons until tomorrow. Now those people are entitled to say to us: 'What! You claim to be French, and you can neither speak nor write your language!' In all this, my poor Frantz, you are not the guiltiest one. We all have our fair share of reproaches to address to ourselves.

"Your parents have not been careful enough to see that you were educated. They preferred to send you to work in the fields or in the factories, in order to have a few more sous. And have I nothing to reproach myself for? Have I not often made you water my garden instead of studying? And when I wanted to go fishing for trout, have I ever hesitated to dismiss you?"

Then, passing from one thing to another, Monsieur Hamel began to talk to us about the French language, saying that it was the most beautiful language in the world, the most clear, the most substantial; that we must always retain it among ourselves, and never forget it, because when a people falls into servitude, "so long as it clings to its language, it is as if it held the key to its prison." Then he took the grammar and read us our lesson. I was amazed to see how readily I understood. Everything that he said seemed so easy to me, so easy. I believed, too, that I had never listened so closely, and that he, for his part, had never been so patient with his explanations. One would have said that, before going away, the poor man desired to give us all his knowledge, to force it all into our heads at a single blow.

When the lesson was at an end, we passed to writing. For that day Monsieur Hamel had prepared some entirely new examples, on which was written in a fine, round hand: "France, Alsace, France, Alsace." They were like little flags, waving all about the class, hanging from the rods of our desks. You should have seen how hard we all worked and how silent it was! Nothing could be heard save the grinding of the pens over the paper. At one time some cockchafers flew in; but no one paid any attention to them, not even the little fellows, who were struggling with their straight lines, with a will and conscientious application, as if even the lines were French. On the roof of the schoolhouse, pigeons cooed in low tones, and I said to myself as I listened to them:

"I wonder if they are going to compel them to sing in German, too!"

From time to time, when I raised my eyes from my paper, I saw Monsieur Hamel sitting motionless in his chair and staring at the objects about him, as if he wished to carry away in his glance the whole of his little school-house. Think of it! For forty years he had been there in the same place, with his yard in front of him and his class just as it was! But the benches and desks were polished and rubbed by use; the walnuts in the yard had grown, and the hopvine which he himself had planted now festooned the windows even to the roof. What a heart-rending thing it must have been for that poor man to leave all those things, and to hear his sister walking back and forth in the room overhead, packing their trunks! For they were to go away the next day—to leave the province forever.

However, he had the courage to keep the class to the end. After the writing, we had the lesson in history; then the little ones sang all together, the ba, be, bi, bo, bu. Yonder, at the back of the room, old Hauser had put on his spectacles, and, holding his spelling book in both hands, he spelled out the letters with them. I could see that he, too, was applying himself. His voice shook with emotion, and it was so funny to hear him, that we all longed to laugh and to cry. Ah! I shall remember that last class.

Suddenly the church clock struck twelve, then the Angelus rang. At the same moment, the bugles of the Prussians returning from drill blared under our windows. Monsieur Hamel rose, pale as death, from his chair. Never had he seemed to me so tall.

"My friends," he said, "my friends, I—I—"

But something suffocated him. He could not finish the sentence. Thereupon he turned to the blackboard, took a piece of chalk, and, bearing on with all his might, wrote in the largest letters he could:

"VIVE LA FRANCE!"

Then he stood there, with his head resting against the wall, and without speaking, he motioned to us with his hand:

"That is all; go."

LESSON 4

EXERCISES

Characterization

Frantz

1. Is Frantz a studious boy, or is he indifferent to school? ______________________

2. As the story progresses, what things does Frantz admit about himself that show how little he has valued his education up until now? ______________________

3. Find at least two examples from the story suggesting that Frantz is easily distracted from his studies. ______________________

Monsieur Hamel

4. How long has Monsieur Hamel been teaching in the village? ______________________

5. What object does he usually carry under his arm? ______________________

6. What does this object reveal about M. Hamel's character? Is he usually a stern or a gentle teacher? ______________________

7. What details does Monsieur Hamel mention to show how he has been an inattentive teacher?

8. How is he dressed on this particular day? ______________________

9. When does he usually wear these clothes? ______________________________

____

____

Old Hauser

10. The character of "old Hauser" is not as clearly portrayed as that of Frantz and Monsieur Hamel, but we can still discover some things about the type of person he is. Does he often come to the schoolhouse? ______________________________

____

11. What object has he brought with him on this day? ______________________________

____

12. Toward the end of the story, we see Hauser trying to learn along with the students. What does this say about his level of education? ______________________________

____

13. Hauser probably did not take his lessons seriously when he was a boy. Which other character does this remind you of? ______________________________

____

Alsatians and Villagers

14. After Frantz is unable to recite the rule about participles, what comparison does Monsieur Hamel make between Frantz and the people of Alsace? ______________________________

____

____

15. What does Monsieur Hamel say that the parents in the village have valued more than the education of their children? ______________________________

____

16. Aside from Hauser, what other characters are present in the back of the schoolhouse?

____

____

____

Plot

17. The background conflict for this story is man versus man—France versus Prussia. Consider the details which indicate that Alsace has already been conquered by Prussia:

    a. Whom does Frantz hear practicing their drills? ______

    b. Why must German be taught in the school? ______

    c. Whose bugles sound under the classroom window? ______

18. As the story opens, why is Frantz running? ______

______

19. What things tempt him to skip school? ______

______

______

______

20. From what we learn as the story progresses, would it have been in character if Frantz had skipped school on this day? ______

______

21. As he goes to school, Frantz expects the day to be like any other day. List at least three things that he experiences that indicate that something is different. ______

______

______

______

______

______

22. After Monsieur Hamel's announcement, why does Frantz suddenly feel angry with himself?

______

______

______

23. What kind of conflict is embodied in Frantz' anger toward himself? ______

______

24. According to Frantz' interpretation, why has Monsieur Hamel put on his fine Sunday clothes?

25. What reasons does Frantz give to explain the fact that Hauser, the ex-mayor, the ex-postman, and some of the other villagers are attending the class?

26. Frantz says that the sight of old Hauser trying to recite his lessons along with the students made them want to laugh and cry. When they look at this pitiful old man who is unable to spell, what fears might they have about themselves?

27. It soon becomes apparent that the characters are motivated to change. Describe at least two things that Frantz observes that illustrate the changed attitude of the people in the classroom.

28. Frantz, Monsieur Hamel, and the villagers in the back of the room have suddenly been forced to face the flaws in their own characters that have led to their loss of freedom. Into what category of conflict would you place this struggle?

29. At the climax of the action, Monsieur Hamel is overcome by emotion. What feeling inspires him to write "*VIVE LA FRANCE*" (*Long live France*) on the board?

Theme

30. Choose the statement below that most accurately expresses the overall theme of the story. Then label the other statements as too general or too specific.

a. ____________________ Time is a precious gift.

b. ____________________ We often come to appreciate things only after we have lost them.

c. ____________________ The people of Alsace gained a sense of patriotism only after losing their freedom.

St. Joan d'Arc

Mary Lynch

Chapter 4

During the three years that Joan heard her Voices, her mother worried about Joan's change in demeanor. She knew Joan was very devout, attending Mass several days a week. Joan often walked two miles away from Domremy to a chapel dedicated to Our Lady. Joan loved it because it had a miraculous statue of the Blessed Mother and her Son, Our Lord Jesus. Thus, Isabelle knew the Catholic faith was a great joy and comfort to Joan.

Isabelle wondered if Joan's seriousness came from her concern for France and for Domremy. She thought about their little village. Domremy was at a crossroads of France, on the way to several large cities. Many travelers came through town, including French soldiers tired of fighting the English. Lately, there had been roving bands of vagabond soldiers in town, claiming to be English. They pretended to be English soldiers, raiding helpless little hamlets like Domremy, but were really just thieves.

Joan was only fourteen when the villagers knew they must do something about these raids. They consulted with each other and decided to meet with the pastor after Sunday Mass. After a special prayer for God's guidance, they discussed their problem.

Finally, Joan's father said, "I think we should evacuate the village."

Another villager said, "Yes, we should, but where can we go?" He shook his head and threw up his hands hopelessly.

Another father added, "Ahh, where? With our wives and children, our babies—where?"

Other voices chimed in. All said the same things.

"Listen!" said Jack d'Arc, waving his hands for silence. "Remember that island where we swam as children?"

The villagers all cried out together in excitement:

"Oh, yes! With all the trees—"

"And some rabbits and squirrels?"

"With the snakes?"

"That's the one!" cried d'Arc.

"But that belongs to the French Army captain, Robert of Baudricourt."

“He owns all the lands we live on, including the island, and perhaps he will rent it to us when he hears why we want it. I have a little money. Maybe if we all pitched in—”

“That’s a good idea,” cried another. “I have some money as well.” The others nodded and agreed to the plan.

Quickly, the men returned to their homes with their news for evacuation of Domremy, in the case of another terrible raid. Captain Baudricourt offered the use of the island free of charge when he heard why they wanted it, but the Domremy villagers were too proud. They insisted on paying rent.

Not long after these arrangements had been made, a French soldier galloped into Domremy, calling loudly that a band of roving thieves was only a day away. The villagers had stored supplies on the island and built several huts for their families. Now, they had to move themselves and their belongings on the island.

They quickly gathered themselves and their animals on boats and rafts to cross over to the island. They did not know how long they might be there, so they took as much food and as many supplies as they could. After a safe arrival, they knelt and prayed to God for their safety.

Late that night, they began to hear shouts and clamor of horses and clank of armor. The villagers did not dare light any fires for food or heat because the brigands might see them. The families huddled in their huts for comfort and warmth all night. Only the children slept. Their animals were hidden among the brush and trees. The noise from Domremy continued all night, and as light from burning houses reflected on the river, each person wondered if it was his house that burned. They groaned and prayed. Finally the noise subsided, but the flames continued to rage through the night.

Jack d’Arc huddled close with his family all through the black night.

“We will rely on Our Lord for our safety,” he told them. “We will say the Rosary.”

Joan took her Rosary from her pocket and set up her little statue of the Blessed Mother and her Son. It was the first thing she had packed for the escape from the thieves.

“Good for you, Joan!” said her father.

With the first light of dawn, they heard more commotion in their village; it was the raiders leaving Domremy. Still, the villagers waited until late afternoon before returning to their homes. Great dismay filled their poor hearts when they saw the damage.

“Oh-h-h! Our church—how could they burn our church?”

“Look at my house! There’s nothing left! Look at our fireplace! All our pots and dishes are broken and blackened from fire!”

“Those devils! They destroyed my house! And they have trampled all my garden!”

“Look at my flowers! All torn up!”

“Oh-h-h! Poor James—he was too lame to go with us, and they killed him in his bed!” The villagers of Domremy gathered around the lifeless body of the old man. The priest immediately started praying over him and the people all knelt.

“Dear Heavenly Father, receive the soul of this dear friend who loved Thee. He was a good Catholic. He went to Mass every Sunday and whenever he could. Let him into Thy glory, O Blessed Trinity, where we all hope to be some day! Let us all join in the Our Father for our friend, James."

The villagers knelt and joined in prayer for this old man who, though always poor, was richest now in Heaven with God and His angels and saints.

After the prayers, everyone began lamenting again about their great losses.

"How are we going to repair anything? They even destroyed our tools!"

"Those terrible soldiers, pretending to be English! They are just robbers!"

"But the English encourage them!"

"Ohh, that duke of Burgundy, who calls himself French, but helps the English!"

"Yes, the traitor—he would rule France himself, and take the throne from the true heir!"

"King Charles of France—he is our king! Charles the Seventh!"

"Ah-h-h! But so young! Only seventeen years old, and surrounded by weaklings—if only we could help him, encourage him to hide no longer!" The people of Domremy were true Frenchmen.

For Joan, the past year of war and turmoil was also the second year of conversation with her "Voices." Now, she began hearing a more specific message from all three saints:

"Save France!"

Joan hated how the English were trying to tear out the heart of her beloved France. Even so, when the saints began telling her to "Save France," she said to them: "I am only a village girl! I know nothing of war! I can't fight with a sword! I can ride a farm horse, but soldiers frighten me!" Joan would have been happy to live the rest of her life in her little village, doing chores and saying her prayers.

"Daughter of God, you must leave your village and save France!"

Joan was still bewildered. She wanted France to be free from the English; but how could a farm girl help?

QUESTIONS

1. Why must the Domremy villagers hide on the island? ____________________
____
____

2. Who owns the island? ____________________
____

3. What message does Joan begin to hear from the saints? ____________________
____
____
____

LESSON 5

"An Angel in Disguise"
T. S. Arthur

Idleness, vice, and intemperance had done their miserable work, and the dead mother lay cold and still amid her wretched children. She had fallen upon the threshold of her own door in a drunken fit, and died in the presence of her frightened little ones.

Death touches the spring of our common humanity. This woman had been despised, scoffed at, and angrily denounced by nearly every man, woman, and child in the village; but now, as the fact of her death was passed from lip to lip, in subdued tones, pity took the place of anger, and sorrow of denunciation. Neighbors went hastily to the old tumble-down hut, in which she had secured little more than a place of shelter from summer heats and winter cold: some with grave-clothes for a decent interment of the body; and some with food for the half-starving children, three in number. Of these, John, the oldest, a boy of twelve, was a stout lad, able to earn his living with any farmer. Kate, between ten and eleven, was a bright, active girl, out of whom something clever might be made, if in good hands; but poor little Maggie, the youngest, was hopelessly diseased. Two years before, a fall from a window had injured her spine, and she had not been able to leave her bed since, except when lifted in the arms of her mother.

"What is to be done with the children?" That was the chief question now. The dead mother would go underground, and be forever beyond all care or concern of the villagers. But the children must not be left to starve. After considering the matter, and talking it over with his wife, farmer Jones said that he would take John, and do well by him, now that his mother was out of the way; and Mrs. Ellis, who had been looking out for a bound girl, concluded that it would be charitable in her to make choice of Katy, even though she was too young to be of much use for several years.

"I could do much better, I know," said Mrs. Ellis; "but as no one seems inclined to take her, I must act from a sense of duty. I expect to have trouble with the child; for she's an undisciplined thing—used to having her own way."

But no one said "I'll take Maggie." Pitying glances were cast on her wan and wasted form and thoughts were troubled on her account. Mothers brought cast-off garments and, removing her soiled and ragged clothes, dressed her in clean attire. The sad eyes and patient face of the little one touched many hearts, and even knocked at them for entrance. But none opened to take her in. Who wanted a bed-ridden child?

"Take her to the poorhouse," said a rough man, of whom the question "What's to be done with Maggie?" was asked. "Nobody's going to be bothered with her."

"The poorhouse is a sad place for a sick and helpless child," answered one.

"For your child or mine," said the other, lightly speaking; "but for this brat it will prove a blessed change; she will be kept clean, have healthy food, and be doctored, which is more than can be said of her past condition."

There was reason in that, but still it didn't satisfy. The day following the day of death was made the day of burial. A few neighbors were at the miserable hovel, but none followed the dead cart as it bore the unhonored remains to its pauper grave. Farmer Jones, after the coffin was taken out, placed John in his wagon and drove away, satisfied that he had done his part. Mrs. Ellis spoke to Kate with a hurried air, "Bid your sister goodbye," and drew the tearful children apart ere scarcely their lips had touched in a sobbing farewell. Hastily others went out, some glancing at Maggie, and some resolutely refraining from a look, until all had gone. She was alone! Just beyond the threshold Joe Thompson, the wheelwright, paused, and said to the blacksmith's wife, who was hastening off with the rest,—

"It's a cruel thing to leave her so."

"Then take her to the poorhouse: she'll have to go there," answered the blacksmith's wife, springing away, and leaving Joe behind.

For a little while the man stood with a puzzled air; then he turned back, and went into the hovel again. Maggie with painful effort, had raised herself to an upright position and was sitting on the bed, straining her eyes upon the door out of which all had just departed. A vague terror had come into her thin white face.

"O, Mr. Thompson!" she cried out, catching her suspended breath, "don't leave me here all alone!"

Though rough in exterior, Joe Thompson, the wheelwright, had a heart, and it was very tender in some places. He liked children, and was pleased to have them come to his shop, where sleds and wagons were made or mended for the village lads without a draft on their hoarded sixpences.

"No, dear," he answered, in a kind voice, going to the bed, and stooping down over the child, "You shan't be left here alone." Then he wrapped her, with the gentleness almost of a woman, in the clean bedclothes which some neighbor had brought; and, lifting her in his strong arms, bore her out into the air and across the field that lay between the hovel and his home.

Now, Joe Thompson's wife, who happened to be childless, was not a woman of saintly temper, nor much given to self-denial for others' good, and Joe had well-grounded doubts touching the manner of greeting he should receive on his arrival. Mrs. Thompson saw him approaching from the window, and with ruffling feathers met him a few paces from the door, as he opened the garden gate, and came in. He bore a precious burden, and he felt it to be so. As his arms held the sick child to his breast, a sphere of tenderness went out from her, and penetrated his feelings. A bond had already corded itself around them both, and love was springing into life.

"What have you there?" sharply questioned Mrs. Thompson.

Joe felt the child start and shrink against him. He did not reply, except by a look that was pleading and cautionary, that said, "Wait a moment for explanations, and be gentle"; and, passing in, carried Maggie to the small chamber on the first floor, and laid her on a bed. Then, stepping back, he shut the door, and stood face to face with his vinegar-tempered wife in the passage-way outside.

"You haven't brought home that sick brat!" Anger and astonishment were in the tones of Mrs. Joe Thompson; her face was in a flame.

"I think women's hearts are sometimes very hard," said Joe. Usually Joe Thompson got out of his wife's way, or kept rigidly silent and non-combative when she fired up on any subject; it was with some surprise, therefore, that she now encountered a firmly set countenance and a resolute pair of eyes.

"Women's hearts are not half so hard as men's!"

Joe saw, by a quick intuition, that his resolute bearing had impressed his wife and he answered quickly, and with real indignation, "Be that as it may, every woman at the funeral turned her eyes steadily from the sick child's face, and when the cart went off with her dead mother, hurried away, and left her alone in that old hut, with the sun not an hour in the sky."

"Where were John and Kate?" asked Mrs. Thompson.

"Farmer Jones tossed John into his wagon, and drove off. Katie went home with Mrs. Ellis; but nobody wanted the poor sick one. 'Send her to the poorhouse,' was the cry."

"Why didn't you let her go, then. What did you bring her here for?"

"She can't walk to the poorhouse," said Joe; "somebody's arms must carry her, and mine are strong enough for that task."

"Then why didn't you keep on? Why did you stop here?" demanded the wife.

"Because I'm not apt to go on fools' errands. The Guardians must first be seen, and a permit obtained."

There was no gainsaying this.

"When will you see the Guardians?" was asked, with irrepressible impatience.

"Tomorrow."

"Why put it off till tomorrow? Go at once for the permit, and get the whole thing off of your hands tonight."

"Jane," said the wheelwright, with an impressiveness of tone that greatly subdued his wife, "I read in the Bible sometimes, and find much said about little children. How the Savior rebuked the disciples who would not receive them; how he took them up in his arms, and blessed them; and how he said that 'whosoever gave them even a cup of cold water should not go unrewarded.' Now, it is a small thing for us to keep this poor motherless little one for a single night; to be kind to her for a single night; to make her life comfortable for a single night."

The voice of the strong, rough man shook, and he turned his head away, so that the moisture in his eyes might not be seen. Mrs. Thompson did not answer, but a soft feeling crept into her heart.

"Look at her kindly, Jane; speak to her kindly," said Joe. "Think of her dead mother, and the loneliness, the pain, the sorrow that must be in all her coming life." The softness of his heart gave unwonted eloquence to his lips.

Mrs. Thompson did not reply, but presently turned towards the little chamber where her husband had deposited Maggie; and, pushing open the door, went quietly in. Joe did not follow; he saw that her state had changed, and felt that it would be best to leave her alone with the child. So he went to his shop, which stood near the house, and worked until dusky evening released him from labor. A light shining through the little chamber window was the first object that attracted Joe's attention on turning towards the house: it was a good omen. The path led him by this window and, when opposite, he could not help pausing to look in. It was now dark enough outside to screen him from observation. Maggie lay, a little raised on the pillow with the lamp shining full upon her face. Mrs. Thompson was sitting by the bed, talking to the child; but her back was towards the window, so that her countenance was not seen. From Maggie's face, therefore, Joe must read the character of their intercourse. He saw that her eyes were intently fixed upon his wife; that now and then a few words came, as if in answers from her lips; that her expression was sad and tender; but he saw nothing of bitterness or pain. A deep-drawn breath was followed by one of relief, as a weight lifted itself from his heart.

On entering, Joe did not go immediately to the little chamber. His heavy tread about the kitchen brought his wife somewhat hurriedly from the room where she had been with Maggie. Joe thought it best not to refer to the child, nor to manifest any concern in regard to her.

"How soon will supper be ready?" he asked.

"Right soon," answered Mrs. Thompson, beginning to bustle about. There was no asperity in her voice.

After washing from his hands and face the dust and soil of work, Joe left the kitchen, and went to the little bedroom. A pair of large bright eyes looked up at him from the snowy bed; looked at him tenderly, gratefully, pleadingly. How his heart swelled in his bosom! With what a quicker motion came the heart-beats! Joe sat down, and now, for the first time, examining the thin face carefully under the lamp light, saw that it was an attractive face, and full of a childish sweetness which suffering had not been able to obliterate.

"Your name is Maggie?" he said, as he sat down and took her soft little hand in his.

"Yes, sir." Her voice struck a chord that quivered in a low strain of music.

"Have you been sick long?"

"Yes, sir." What a sweet patience was in her tone!

"Has the doctor been to see you?"

"He used to come."

"But not lately?"

"No, sir."

"Have you any pain?"

"Sometimes, but not now."

"When had you pain?"

"This morning my side ached, and my back hurt when you carried me."

"It hurts you to be lifted or moved about?"

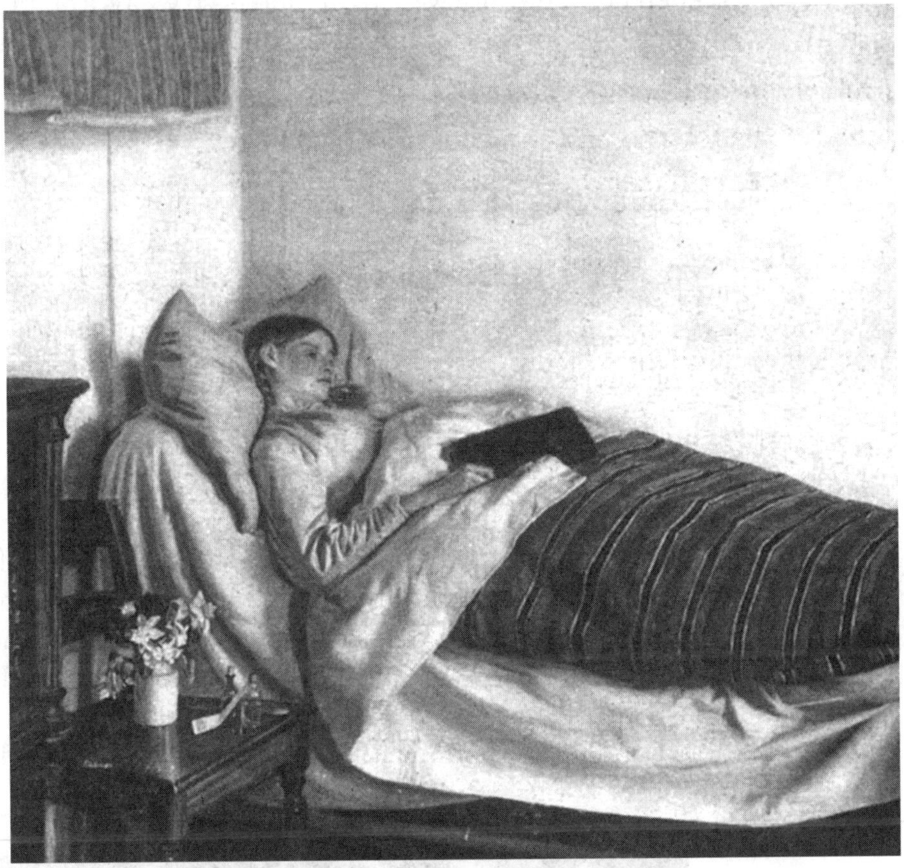

"Yes, sir."

"Your side doesn't ache now?"

"No, sir."

"Does it ache a great deal?"

"Yes, sir; but it hasn't ached any since I've been on this soft bed."

"The soft bed feels good."

"O, yes, sir—so good!" What a satisfaction, mingled with gratitude, was in her voice!

"Supper is ready," said Mrs. Thompson, looking into the room a little while afterwards.

Joe glanced from his wife's face to that of Maggie; she understood him, and answered,—

"She can wait until we are done; then I will bring her something to eat." There was an effort at indifference on the part of Mrs. Thompson, but her husband had seen her through the window, and understood that the coldness was assumed. Joe waited, after sitting down to the table, for his wife to introduce the subject uppermost in both of their thoughts; but she kept silent on that theme, for many minutes, and he maintained a like reserve. At last she said, abruptly,—

"What are you going to do with that child?"

"I thought you understood me that she was to go to the poorhouse," replied Joe, as if surprised at her question.

Mrs. Thompson looked rather strangely at her husband for some moments, and then dropped her eyes. The subject was not again referred to during the meal. At its close, Mrs. Thompson toasted a slice of bread, and softened it with milk and butter; adding to this a cup of tea, she took them in to Maggie, and held the small waiter, on which she had placed them, while the hungry child ate with every sign of pleasure.

"Is it good?" asked Mrs. Thompson, seeing with what a keen relish the food was taken.

The child paused with the cup in her hand, and answered with a look of gratitude that awoke to new life old human feelings which had been slumbering in her heart for half a score of years.

"We'll keep her a day or two longer; she is so weak and helpless," said Mrs. Joe Thompson, in answer to her husband's remark, at breakfast-time on the next morning, that he must step down and see the Guardians of the Poor about Maggie.

"She'll be so much in your way," said Joe.

"I shan't mind that for a day or two. Poor thing!"

Joe did not see the Guardians of the Poor on that day, on the next, nor on the day following. In fact, he never saw them at all on Maggie's account, for in less than a week Mrs. Joe Thompson would as soon have thought of taking up her own abode in the almshouse as sending Maggie there.

What light and blessing did that sick and helpless child bring to the home of Joe Thompson, the poor wheelwright! It had been dark, and cold, and miserable there for a long time just because his wife had nothing to love and care for out of herself, and so became sour, irritable, ill-tempered, and self-afflicting in the desolation of her woman's nature. Now the sweetness of that sick child, looking ever to her in love, patience, and gratitude, was as honey to her soul, and she carried her in her heart as well as in her arms, a precious burden. As for Joe Thompson, there was not a man in all the neighborhood who drank daily of a more precious wine of life than he. An angel had come into his house, disguised as a sick, helpless, and miserable child, and filled all its dreary chambers with the sunshine of love.

LESSON 5

EXERCISES

Characterization

Write a short character sketch of each of the following people. Include as much information as you can regarding physical description (e.g. child, adult, old person, healthy, sickly, etc.), temperament (e.g. joyful, bitter, even-tempered, etc.), and moral qualities (e.g. selfish, generous, grateful, patient, etc.). If a character undergoes a change, describe the nature of the change.

1. Maggie: ____

____

____

____

2. Mr. Joe Thompson: ____

____

____

____

3. Mrs. Thompson: ____

____

____

____

Plot

4. When Farmer Jones and Mrs. Ellis take in the two older children, what motives other than charity do you think they have? ____

____

____

____

5. The people of the village are unwilling to take Maggie because she is paralyzed. How must they think that caring for Maggie would affect their lives? ______

______

______

6. Joe Thompson has a hard time walking away and leaving Maggie all alone. What are we told about him that illustrates his love of children? ______

______

______

7. When Joe faces his wife after bringing Maggie home, what is unusual about the way he handles himself? ______

______

______

8. What emotion does Mrs. Thompson begin to feel under the influence of her husband's words?

______

9. Once Joe sees that his wife is starting to care for Maggie, he begins to act as though he feels no attachment for the girl and still plans to take her to the poorhouse. What effect does this have on his wife? ______

______

______

Theme

10. Look carefully at the change that Mrs. Thompson experiences, and especially at the way the narrator describes this change in the last paragraph. Think about her experience in relation to the spiritual wisdom contained in the Prayer of Saint Francis:

Lord, make me an instrument of your peace.
Where there is hatred, let me sow love;
where there is injury, pardon;
where there is doubt, faith;
where there is despair, hope;
where there is darkness, light;
where there is sadness, joy.
O Divine Master, grant that I may not so much seek to be consoled as to console;

to be understood as to understand;
to be loved as to love.
For it is in giving that we receive;
it is in pardoning that we are pardoned;
and it is in dying that we are born to eternal life.

Now, choose the statement below that most accurately expresses the overall theme of the story. Label the other statements as too general or too specific. You should use one of the labels twice.

a. ______________________ Love makes the world go 'round.

b. ______________________ An open, generous heart will be repaid in ways never imagined.

c. ______________________ A woman who adopts a disabled child learns the meaning of true happiness.

d. ______________________ Love is the life of the soul.

St. Joan d'Arc

Mary Lynch

Chapter 5

Another year passed after the burning of their village. Joan's Voices continually urged her to save France. She now trusted that God would help her to do so, but still did not understand how it would happen. Isabelle saw that her daughter was preoccupied by some serious matter, but she did not say anything about it. She was sure Joan would come to her eventually with her problem.

One day, several months after her fifteenth birthday, Joan was watching the animals out in the fields when she heard excited shouts from the other side of Domremy. She called to the animals, sent Beau to round up the cows and sheep, and ran as fast as she could back to the village. She met Peter on the way.

"Father sent me to get you, Joan! The English soldiers are coming!" He waved his arms and pointed to the other side of the village.

At the house, their mother was crying and hurriedly gathering clothes for little Catherine. She handed the tot to Joan, saying, "I must gather some food, just in case!"

Joan's father and brother were also hurrying, stuffing clothes and supplies into a sack. Jack reached over the front door and took down the crucifix. Joan rushed to her little bed nook and picked up the statue of Our Blessed Mother.

There were shouts all around as everyone frantically tried to gather what he needed most. Catherine was crying because she saw that everyone was upset.

Just two weeks before, the villagers of Domremy had made arrangements with a village a few miles away. They would go there for safety, in case of a sudden raid. They had to hurry because the soldiers were just about four miles away, on the other side of the village. They were burning and pillaging as they went.

Joan's father put his wife and Catherine in the wagon while Peter hitched their horse Prince to it. Joan jumped up and took the reins.

"The boys and I will run alongside of you!" yelled her father. "We don't want to make the wagon too heavy for Prince!" They had piled as much as they could into the little wagon.

Isabelle had wanted to take her favorite iron cooking pot, too, but her husband said, "No! You don't need that! We'll be at our friend's house! Let's go!"

Once again, families of the town were uprooted and required to stay with friends for three weeks until it was safe to return. When they arrived back in Domremy, little was left of it. They were shocked by the destruction. The animals they had not been able to take with them were now blackened carcasses. Their gardens were destroyed. Everything breakable was broken. Wooden houses and even trees were burned to the ground. All the villagers were crying aloud, weeping silently, or on the fringe of despair.

The d'Arc family home was only a pile of blackened stones. Joan comforted her family, saying,

"We are still alive, and we have our good health! God will help us get everything back together once again!"

"You're right, Joan," said her father, nodding his head. "Let us all say a prayer of thanks that we are still safe together as a family!"

He put their family crucifix on a blackened tree stump, and Joan put her statue of the Blessed Mother next to it. They all knelt down among of the rubble of their home. They blessed themselves. They said the Our Father, the Hail Mary and the Apostles' Creed. Then they stood up, ready for work.

"Let's clear out the debris from the center of our house," Joan's mother said.

Peter found a wooden bucket that was not totally destroyed.

"I'll get some water from the river," he declared.

Joan pulled a blanket from the sack she had brought with her.

"Here, Mother, sit on this blanket with Catherine. I'll try to get some food together for lunch." She spread out another blanket. She put some apples and cheese on it, and also a loaf of bread that they had brought from their friend's home.

After a while, Joan's father and brothers squatted down by the blanket. They said grace and ate a little lunch.

"Don't worry, Isabelle," said Jack to his wife. "We started out without much when we were first married, didn't we? God will provide!" And he kissed his wife. "And now, besides, we have these wonderful children to help us!" Isabelle smiled at everybody, and kissed Jack quickly on the cheek.

After Domremy was burnt, Joan again heard the voices of the saints. For the first time, there was a detailed command for her.

"Daughter of God, go to Robert de Beaudricourt in the town of Vaucouleurs. He will give you men to take you to the true king of France."

Joan knew that she must obey this command, and she felt confident that she could accomplish it with God's help. Rather than being concerned about saving all of France, she could concentrate on this small trip to see their landowner. Her saints were telling her something she could do to help France.

"You will do no such thing!" Joan's father was outraged. His face was red, and his eyebrows met together above his piercing eyes.

It was a few days after the family's return to their village. They still struggled to accept their terrible losses. Although they worked hard to repair the damage to their home, they moaned about the terrible English and the thieves who had been encouraged to attack and destroy the French villages.

The villagers, including the women and children, had held a special meeting. They said something must be done to save France from the English. After the meeting had ended, Joan told her father that she would join the French army to save France.

It was then that he roared, "You will do no such thing!" His irate words upset Joan, but, remembering St. Michael's command, she said, "Father, God Himself wants me to do it!"

Her father stamped his foot at her words. "I would sooner drown you in the river myself than have you join the army!" He stamped his foot again. "I'll hear no more of this craziness!" He stalked away with a growl.

"You must obey your father, Joan dear!" Isabelle said kindly. Joan did not answer, but her mother could see the determined look on Joan's face.

"Joan, why do you think you can save France by joining the army?"

"Because the saints have told me that God wants me to help save France!" Joan's mother was shocked. She suddenly realized what Joan had been keeping secret for the past few years. Now, Joan continued:

"Dear Mama! I'm sorry to surprise you like this, but I did not know what to do or say to you and Father."

"But Joan," said her mother, "you say—God? God wants you to fight for France?"

"Yes, Mama. St. Margaret, St. Catherine and St. Michael, the great Prince of the Heavenly Host, have told me every day for the past three years that I must save France! They say that I am the one to do it. I must do as they say."

"But how can you? A simple country girl—" Joan's mother stopped speaking. She was stunned.

"I know that, Mama! But now they have told me what to do." Then Joan explained to her mother about the plan for meeting the heir to the French throne. While her father was still away, Joan told her mother about when the saints spoke to her, and everything they said.

"My darling, Joan! I knew there was something on your mind, and that some day you would tell me!" She hugged Joan tightly. Isabelle's faith was so strong that she recognized truth when she heard it. She knew she was hearing truth from Joan.

Joan's father returned later, in time for the evening's supper. He did not say a word about Joan joining the French army. Joan's mother said nothing, and neither did Joan. Joan's brothers and sister had not been home when Joan's father forbade her to join the army, but their mother whispered the news to them. They noticed their father was forcefully cheerful. He talked about everything except Joan's desire to join the army. As they went to sleep that night, Joan's brothers decided that she must be crazy. Joan's mother could only think to herself, "What is God's will?"

QUESTIONS

1. The conflict between the French and English is a man versus ____________________ conflict.

2. Once Joan announces her desire to join the French army, she meets different kinds of opposition from her family. Briefly tell how each person listed below reacts to her plan:

   a. Father: ____

   ____

   b. Mother: ____

   ____

   c. Brothers: ____

   ____

JESUS MARIE
S. JOAN OF ARC

LESSON 6

"The Selfish Giant"
Oscar Wilde

Every afternoon, as they were coming from school, the children used to go and play in the Giant's garden.

It was a large lovely garden, with soft green grass. Here and there over the grass stood beautiful flowers like stars, and there were twelve peach trees that in the spring-time broke out into delicate blossoms of pink and pearl, and in the autumn bore rich fruit. The birds sat on the trees and sang so sweetly that the children used to stop their games in order to listen to them. "How happy we are here!" they cried to each other.

One day the Giant came back. He had been to visit his friend the Cornish ogre, and had stayed with him for seven years. After the seven years were over he had said all that he had to say, for his conversation was limited, and he determined to return to his own castle. When he arrived he saw the children playing in the garden.

"What are you doing here?" he cried in a very gruff voice, and the children ran away.

"My own garden is my own garden," said the Giant; "any one can understand that, and I will allow nobody to play in it but myself." So he built a high wall all round it, and put up a notice-board.

TRESPASSERS
WILL BE
PROSECUTED

He was a very selfish Giant.

The poor children had now nowhere to play. They tried to play on the road, but the road was very dusty and full of hard stones, and they did not like it. They used to wander round the high wall when their lessons were over, and talk about the beautiful garden inside. "How happy we were there," they said to each other.

Then the Spring came, and all over the country there were little blossoms and little birds. Only in the garden of the Selfish Giant it was still winter. The birds did not care to sing in it as there were no children, and the trees forgot to blossom. Once a beautiful flower put its head out from the grass, but when it saw the notice-board it was so sorry for the children that it slipped back into the ground again, and went off to sleep. The only people who were pleased were the Snow and the Frost. "Spring has forgotten this garden," they cried, "so we will live here all the year round." The Snow covered up the grass with her great white cloak, and the

Frost painted all the trees silver. Then they invited the North Wind to stay with them, and he came. He was wrapped in furs, and he roared all day about the garden, and blew the chimney-pots down. "This is a delightful spot," he said, "we must ask the Hail on a visit." So the Hail came. Every day for three hours he rattled on the roof of the castle till he broke most of the slates, and then he ran round and round the garden as fast as he could go. He was dressed in grey, and his breath was like ice.

"I cannot understand why the Spring is so late in coming," said the Selfish Giant, as he sat at the window and looked out at his cold white garden; "I hope there will be a change in the weather."

But the Spring never came, nor the Summer. The Autumn gave golden fruit to every garden, but to the Giant's garden she gave none. "He is too selfish," she said. So it was always Winter there, and the North Wind, and the Hail, and the Frost, and the Snow danced about through the trees.

One morning the Giant was lying awake in bed when he heard some lovely music. It sounded so sweet to his ears that he thought it must be the King's musicians passing by. It was really only a little linnet singing outside his window, but it was so long since he had heard a bird sing in his garden that it seemed to him to be the most beautiful music in the world. Then the Hail stopped dancing over his head, and the North Wind ceased roaring, and a delicious perfume came to him through the open casement. "I believe the Spring has come at last," said the Giant; and he jumped out of bed and looked out.

What did he see?

He saw a most wonderful sight. Through a little hole in the wall the children had crept in, and they were sitting in the branches of the trees. In every tree that he could see there was a little child. And the trees were so glad to have the children back again that they had covered themselves with blossoms, and were waving their arms gently above the children's heads. The birds were flying about and twittering with delight, and the flowers were looking up through the green grass and laughing. It was a lovely scene, only in one corner it was still winter. It was the farthest corner of the garden, and in it was standing a little boy. He was so small that

he could not reach up to the branches of the tree, and he was wandering all round it, crying bitterly. The poor tree was still quite covered with frost and snow, and the North Wind was blowing and roaring above it. "Climb up! little boy," said the Tree, and it bent its branches down as low as it could; but the boy was too tiny.

And the Giant's heart melted as he looked out. "How selfish I have been!" he said; "now I know why the Spring would not come here. I will put that poor little boy on the top of the tree, and then I will knock down the wall, and my garden shall be the children's playground for ever and ever." He was really very sorry for what he had done.

So he crept downstairs and opened the front door quite softly, and went out into the garden. But when the children saw him they were so frightened that they all ran away, and the garden became winter again. Only the little boy did not run, for his eyes were so full of tears that he did not see the Giant coming. And the Giant stole up behind him and took him gently in his hand, and put him up into the tree. And the tree broke at once into blossom, and the birds came and sang on it, and the little boy stretched out his two arms and flung them round the Giant's neck, and kissed him. And the other children, when they saw that the Giant was not wicked any longer, came running back, and with them came the Spring. "It is your garden now, little children," said the Giant, and he took a great axe and knocked down the wall. And when the people were going to market at twelve o'clock they found the Giant playing with the children in the most beautiful garden they had ever seen.

All day long they played, and in the evening they came to the Giant to bid him good-bye.

"But where is your little companion?" he said: "the boy I put into the tree." The Giant loved him the best because he had kissed him.

"We don't know," answered the children; "he has gone away."

"You must tell him to be sure and come here to-morrow," said the Giant. But the children said that they did not know where he lived, and had never seen him before; and the Giant felt very sad.

Every afternoon, when school was over, the children came and played with the Giant. But the little boy whom the Giant loved was never seen again. The Giant was very kind to all the children, yet he longed for his first little friend, and often spoke of him. "How I would like to see him!" he used to say.

Years went over, and the Giant grew very old and feeble. He could not play about any more, so he sat in a huge armchair, and watched the children at their games, and admired his garden. "I have many beautiful flowers," he said; "but the children are the most beautiful flowers of all."

One winter morning he looked out of his window as he was dressing. He did not hate the Winter now, for he knew that it was merely the Spring asleep, and that the flowers were resting.

Suddenly he rubbed his eyes in wonder, and looked and looked. It certainly was a marvellous sight. In the farthest corner of the garden was a tree quite covered with lovely white blossoms. Its branches were all golden, and silver fruit hung down from them, and underneath it stood the little boy he had loved.

Downstairs ran the Giant in great joy, and out into the garden. He hastened across the grass, and came near to the child. And when he came quite close his face grew red with anger, and he said, “Who hath dared to wound thee?” For on the palms of the child’s hands were the prints of two nails, and the prints of two nails were on the little feet.

“Who hath dared to wound thee?” cried the Giant; “tell me, that I may take my big sword and slay him.”

“Nay!” answered the child; “but these are the wounds of Love.”

“Who art thou?” said the Giant, and a strange awe fell on him, and he knelt before the little child.

And the child smiled on the Giant, and said to him, “You let me play once in your garden, to-day you shall come with me to my garden, which is Paradise.”

And when the children ran in that afternoon, they found the Giant lying dead under the tree, all covered with white blossoms.

LESSON 6

EXERCISES

Characterization

Most of the characters in "The Selfish Giant" are really symbols; in other words, they represent someone or something else. While you were reading this story, perhaps you thought about certain characters and ideas from the Bible or from your own knowledge of the Faith. Match each character or group of characters below to its appropriate reference.

______	1. The Selfish Giant	A. Christ the Redeemer
______	2. the children playing in the garden, then banished	B. Creation renewed by the grace of God
______	3. the mysterious little boy	C. The human heart when it rejects God's love and the love of neighbor
______	4. Winter in the garden without the children	D. Fallen creation
______	5. Spring in the garden when the children return	E. Adam and Eve

Plot

6. When the Selfish Giant sees the children playing in the garden, he realizes how selfish he has been and repents. What does he decide to do as his first act of unselfishness?

____

____

7. This story contains two climaxes. The first comes when the Selfish Giant ceases to be selfish and learns to love. What constitutes the second climax, when the Giant has truly won the battle forever? ____

____

____

8. Into which category would you place the main conflict in this story? (See p ix) Why? ________

____

____

9. What happens at the very end that is a sign to the children that all is well with the Giant? ______

____

____

____

The plot of "The Selfish Giant" is symbolic, like its characters. Although the parallels are not exact, most of the action in the story should remind you of some aspect of salvation history or some truth of the Faith. Match the similar incidents.

______	10. The children play happily and peacefully in the garden before the return of the Selfish Giant.	A. Adam and Eve, and all of their children on earth, live in exile from the Garden of Eden, and long to return.
______	11. Perpetual winter falls upon the garden because of a proud, selfish action.	B. Jesus appeared to his disciples and showed them his wounds.
______	12. The children have nowhere to play but the dusty, stony road, and they long to return to the garden.	C. Before the Fall Adam and Eve lived in perfect happiness.
______	13. The giant awakes one morning to find that the children, including the mysterious little boy, have entered the garden, and Spring has returned.	D. Jesus said to the Good Thief, "Today you will be with me in Paradise."
______	14. After this incident, the little boy disappears until the Giant's death.	E. "Then Simon Peter, who had a sword, drew it and struck the high priest's servant, cutting off his right ear...Jesus commanded Peter, 'Put your sword away! Shall I not drink the cup the Father has given me?'" (John 18:10-11)
______	15. When the little boy returns, he has nail prints in his hands and feet.	F. When Adam and Eve sinned and lost God's grace, all of creation fell with them.
______	16. When the giant sees the little boy's wounds, he wants to take his sword and kill the one who would do such a thing, but the boy rejects this idea.	G. The Second Person of the Blessed Trinity came into the world in His own time and of His own free will to save us, though we were lost in sin.
______	17. The little boy promises that today he will take the giant with him to Paradise.	H. Jesus ascended into Heaven after the Resurrection, and we will not see Him until we die.

Theme

18. The theme of "The Selfish Giant" has to do with selfishness versus love. Spend some time thinking about the idea or message that the author is trying to convey, and then write a statement that could serve as the theme of the story. Remember that a theme must be:

    a. broad enough to apply to life in general, but without being too vague (e.g. "Selfishness is bad," or "God's love saves us," would not be good statements of theme).

    b. specific enough to apply to this particular story, but without recounting specific events or naming particular characters or objects (e.g. don't mention the giant, the children, the garden, the building of a wall, etc.).

St. Joan d'Arc

Mary Lynch

Chapter 6

Joan felt terrible about upsetting her father, and she decided not to mention the army again. Still, she felt that she must obey God. It just so happened that at that time Joan had a cousin who was expecting a baby, to be born in about three months. This cousin lived in a nearby village. Joan did what she had done before for her cousin. She went to visit her to help her until her baby was to be born.

The little village where Joan's cousin lived was very close to the town of Vaucouleurs, where Robert of Baudricourt lived. This was the man that the saints had told Joan to go to see in order to save France.

It would be unsafe for a young girl to travel alone in those times, so Joan persuaded her uncle to take her to visit Robert of Baudricourt. A few weeks after the new baby came, Joan and her uncle traveled to Vaucouleurs.

The castle of Baudricourt was built of massive gray stones, had tall towers for defense, and was surrounded by a moat. It was three stories high and spread out at the crest of a small hill to about the length of two football fields. There were soldiers stationed all around the castle—a protection from the same English-led marauders that had stormed Domremy.

When Joan and her uncle arrived at Baudricourt, they were met at the front gate by a guard, who rang a large bell hanging on the wall. This brought the major-domo of the castle, George. He handled much of Captain Robert's business, such as signing papers, paying the servants, ordering housekeeping supplies, and screening people who wanted to visit Captain Robert.

George was impressed by the lovely simplicity of Joan's red, white, and blue peasant dress and by her dignified manner and pleasant smile. Joan's uncle was very polite, and after introducing Joan, let her do the talking. She was able to impress George sufficiently with the seriousness of her message about helping to save France. What could be more serious? He took Joan and her uncle into the castle to see Sir Robert.

The captain was relaxing in his library with some military friends. They were all at ease, but their conversation was about the future of France.

"If we don't stop England now, we shall all be English slaves!" declared one.

George escorted Joan and her uncle into the room. She calmly walked toward the famous, wealthy, and powerful landowner, who sat smoking his favorite pipe. Her uncle was nervous, and stood back by the door.

"So, Joan d'Arc! George tells me you have a plan for saving France! What is it?" Robert chuckled a little as he spoke.

Joan looked at Robert. His hair was black and very short. He had no mustache or beard, but his eyebrows were the blackest, biggest, and bushiest that Joan had ever seen. Bright blue eyes peered out from under those eyebrows, which were now arched with his question. His forehead was deeply furrowed, and two deep lines stretched from the sides of his nose down around his mouth. Joan instantly thought that he must be good at ordering soldiers around.

Robert asked Joan again, "What is your message?" She returned his question with a steady gaze and felt the weight of her responsibility to deliver the message from heaven.

"Here is my message to you, Sir Robert of Baudricourt, Governor of Vaucouleurs. You will tell Charles the Dauphin, the uncrowned king of France, to wait and not to fight his enemies, for God will very soon send him help!"

"Charles needs no message like that!" scoffed Robert. "He will wait! You can be sure of that!"

His fellow officers looked at Joan and shook their heads.

"Do you have anything more to say?" growled Robert.

"Yes," said Joan. "I must beg you to give me an escort of men-at-arms and send me to Charles."

"Why?" Robert laughed scornfully.

"So that he can make me his general, to drive the English out of France and to crown him king." Sir Robert could not help smiling, but he placed his hand over his mouth. He recognized Joan's sincerity and her true desire to help France.

"You are just a child!" Robert answered as gently as he could.

"Still, I am appointed to do it." Joan was very dignified and serious.

"And when—" Robert looked around at his officers with a small smile; they were all chuckling. "When will this happen that Charles will be crowned?"

"Next year! And he will be master of France!"

Then Robert asked somewhat gruffly, "Who sent you with this ridiculous message?"

"My Lord."

"What Lord?" Robert asked.

"The King of Heaven!" answered Joan.

At this, Robert roared to George, "Take her away—and give her a whipping!"

Joan quickly stepped back, but then she turned to Sir Robert and said, "You refuse me the soldiers—why? For it is My Lord God Who has commanded you! Yes, He made the command, and so I must come again. And more times, perhaps, but I shall have the men-at-arms, because it is God's will!"

Then Joan and her uncle left the room and were escorted from the castle.

Sir Robert of Baudricourt was a tough, battle-hardened soldier. He had fought his way through France against the English, but after constant losses was now disappointed and discouraged. The rightful king of France, Charles the Dauphin (Doh-fan), did not fight. He and his court remained safe in southern France, on land he had inherited from his father, King Charles VI.

Robert's discouragement made him retire to his castle and hope for the best. He felt helpless. He was disgusted with everything and everybody, especially his king. Now, this young girl had the nerve to tell him that she could save France! He felt mocked.

Still, Robert began to think about Joan's message. She had seemed mature and sincere, but why would God depend on a young girl to save France? It did not make sense to him. Because Robert was a good Catholic, he decided to pray about what Joan had told him. He must have thought about the fact that Mary, the Mother of God, was a young girl like Joan when she took on the highest responsibility of any human being, that of being the Mother of the Son of God.

Sir Robert had a large household. Besides the major-domo, George, there were soldiers who guarded the gates, a cook and her assistants, groundskeepers, gardeners, stable boys, and maids. All the castle workers had families living in the surrounding village. When George told the soldier at the gate that Joan declared that God wanted her to save France, Joan's message went like lightning through the castle, out to the village, and then to the nearby villages. In two days, the whole area was talking about the young girl whom God had sent to save France. Even the officers who were with Robert when Joan gave him the Lord's message talked about it with their families and friends.

After Sir Robert's strong dismissal, Joan did not return home. She decided that since God's saints had told her to talk to Sir Robert about saving France, God would arrange for him to change his mind. So she stayed in the village with friends and relatives.

The villagers started coming to see her, to pray for her, and to encourage her to go to war for France. The villagers accepted her word that God sent His saints to her to tell her to save France. They were so strong in their belief of Joan's saintliness, that some even brought their sick children for her to cure them. We have no record of any miracle she might have performed, but her prayers for them must have been heard by God. All this went on for about six weeks.

Then Joan's saints told her it was getting late for saving France. So she went to see Sir Robert again; he was ready to talk with her about God's plan to save France. Robert had received many notes and messages from the villagers, all urging him to help Joan "Save France!" Still, he was a very careful man, both about his own personal business and about Holy Mother Church.

When Joan arrived at the castle, Sir Robert had the local priest with him. He wanted to be certain that Joan's messages were not from the devil. The priest put on his stole, the narrow purple silk band that a priest wears around his neck for hearing confession. He told Joan to leave them if she were from the devil, but to approach them if her inspirations were from God. Joan fell to her knees, and on her knees quietly approached them. At this, the priest and Robert de Baudricourt took her hands and gently kissed them.

Then Joan said quietly but strongly, "I must go to Charles, heir to the throne of France! Haven't you heard the prophecy that France would be saved by a maiden from the Province of Lorraine? My saints have told me that Charles, the Dauphin, must be crowned king of France!"

Robert still hesitated to send Joan to Charles. However, after two more French battle losses, he finally agreed to do so.

Joan thought she must dress like the soldiers she would be among in the French army. She was fitted for white armor which she selected herself. She had her hair cut like the soldiers of the time. The cut looked like a bowl was placed on top of her head, and all hair showing below it was cut off. Her hair hung perfectly straight to her eyebrows, the top of her ears, and halfway down the back of her head.

In spite of this haircut, when Joan sat on her big black horse with her white armor, her pale skin, and the blue eyes below her black hair, she was beautiful. Above all, it was easy for the soldiers to see her.

So Joan and her entourage rode to Chinon (Shee-nohn), where the Dauphin Charles was holding his court. His castle was not far from the city of Orléans (Or-lay-Ahn).

It was a dangerous journey to the king. Joan and her guards met English soldiers who believed, because of the grace of God, that Joan's little group were English, too. They went safely on to the town of Chinon.

As they approached the town, practically everyone came out to meet the "Maiden," as Joan called herself. People crowded closely around her, asking for her blessing. They were already calling her a saint, for they knew that God's great saints spoke with her. They were filled with the joy of her presence.

Finally, Joan went to the castle of Chinon to meet the future king. It was evening when she arrived. There was a crowd of people gathered in the great ballroom with Charles. They were eager to see and hear the "Maiden" whom all the villagers were talking about.

Joan had never seen Charles and did not know what he looked like. At this moment, he was not wearing his crown. Nevertheless, Joan walked straight through the bustling ballroom and knelt at Charles's feet. She stared into his large brown eyes, and he stared into her blue ones. The Dauphin was quite thin, his face almost gaunt. Although not handsome, he had a wonderful, wide smile.

"I am Joan the Maiden," Joan began. "God has sent me to help you and your kingdom. You shall be anointed king and crowned in the city of Rheims [Ram]. And you shall be the lieutenant of the King of Heaven, who is the King of France!"

Charles believed Joan because she told him what he had been secretly praying about. He was certain that Joan was sent to him by God because she told him St. Michael had sent her. Just a short time before, Charles had dedicated France to St. Michael.

However, Charles was very cautious. He called a special committee of clergy to interrogate her. These learned churchmen declared Joan to be "humble, pure, honest, and simple."

Joan met all kinds of people with the king, and many more wanted to meet her. However, Joan had come to the Dauphin to help him fight for France. It was not long before he allowed her to lead the French army into battle.

Joan was assigned a soldier as her standard-bearer. Her standard was a stiff, heavy square of cloth called buckram. It was white with gold fringe around the edges. On one side of the standard was a picture of God, King of Heaven, holding the world with one hand and blessing it with the other. The archangels Gabriel and Michael were shown offering God a lily. At the top were the names "Jesus" and "Mary" in gold letters. On the other side of Joan's standard was pictured a silver dove. In its beak was a streamer with the words, "King of Heaven."

As she rode into battle, Joan carried her own personal "pennon." This was a small triangular flag, also in white. It displayed a picture of Our Lady with an angel kneeling in front of her, offering her a lily. A local sign-painter had painted both of these flags.

Joan had a miraculous sword attached to her armor. Joan's Voices had told her to have priests look under the altar of a certain church to find it. Although no one had heard of the sword's existence before, the priests found it there, just as Joan had told them they would. She wore the sword into battle, but she never used it. Later, when the English questioned Joan at her trial, she was able to say, "I never killed anyone!"

In her white armor and on a black horse, Joan could be seen by all the French soldiers. They followed her without question as she led them into combat. The soldiers were convinced that she was sent to them by God to save France, and they charged forward in battle like they had never done before.

"Allez, mes enfants! Allez vite, mes soldats! Dépêchez-vous! A bas avec les Anglais!" Joan shouted to her soldiers, charging forward on her horse at the head of the French Army. "Go, my children! Go quickly, my soldiers! Hurry up! Down with the English!" She kicked her horse hard with her spurs, and he leaped forward.

"Aux Anglais!" Joan shouted again.

As one body, the French army sprang forward behind Joan against the ranks of the English. The English were surprised—during the last hundred years, the French had always retreated in a battle. With this leader from God, though, they were sure to be victorious.

There were many battles, and Joan led the French to victory in all of them. Her saints told her which battles to fight and how to fight them. The French soldiers received Our Lord in Holy Communion before every battle, and Joan forbade them to use Our Lord's Holy Name in vain.

During the battle of Orléans, an English arrow shot into Joan's shoulder. She was knocked down and in terrible pain. Some soldiers carried her away from the action to see to her wound, but a report came that the French were starting to fall back. Without Joan at their front, they had begun to lose heart. So Joan pulled the arrow out herself, leaped back on her horse, and galloped to the front of the fighting. The French were victorious.

Orléans was an important victory for France, and the people of Orléans celebrated with an elaborate parade. They called Joan a saint and threw flowers at her feet as she passed them. Shouts of joy filled the air: "Joan! Joan! The Maiden of Orléans! The saint of God! Thanks to God for the saint! Joan, the Maiden of God!"

QUESTIONS

1. When they first hear Joan's message, why are Sir Robert and his men amused? ____________

____

____

____

2. Underline two miraculous events which show that Joan's mission is divine.

3. What does the arrow incident show about Joan's character? ____________________

____

____

____

LESSON 7

"Dutch Courage"
Jack London

"Just our luck!"

Gus Lafee finished wiping his hands and sullenly threw the towel upon the rocks. His attitude was one of deep dejection. The light seemed gone out of the day and the glory from the golden sun. Even the keen mountain air was devoid of relish, and the early morning no longer yielded its customary zest.

"Just our luck!" Gus repeated, this time avowedly for the edification of another young fellow who was busily engaged in sousing his head in the water of the lake.

"What are you grumbling about, anyway?" Hazard Van Dorn lifted a soap-rimmed face questioningly. His eyes were shut. "What's our luck?"

"Look there!" Gus threw a moody glance skyward. "Some duffer's got ahead of us. We've been scooped, that's all!"

Hazard opened his eyes, and caught a fleeting glimpse of a white flag waving arrogantly on the edge of a wall of rock nearly a mile above his head. Then his eyes closed with a snap, and his face wrinkled spasmodically. Gus threw him the towel, and uncommiseratingly watched him wipe out the offending soap. He felt too blue himself to take stock in trivialities.

Hazard groaned.

"Does it hurt much?" Gus queried, coldly, without interest, as if it were no more than his duty to ask after the welfare of his comrade.

"I guess it does," responded the suffering one.

"Soap's pretty strong, eh? — Noticed it myself."

"'Tisn't the soap. It's-it's that!" He opened his reddened eyes and pointed toward the innocent white little flag. "That's what hurts."

Gus Lafee did not reply, but turned away to start the fire and begin cooking breakfast. His disappointment and grief were too deep for anything but silence, and Hazard, who felt likewise, never opened his mouth as he fed the horses, nor once laid his head against their arching necks or passed caressing fingers through their manes. The two boys were blind, also, to the manifold glories of Mirror Lake which reposed at their very feet. Nine times, had they chosen to move along its margin the short distance of a hundred yards, could they have seen the sunrise repeated; nine times, from behind as many successive peaks, could they have seen the great orb rear his blazing rim; and nine times, had they but looked into the waters of the lake, could they have seen the phenomena reflected faithfully and vividly. But all the titanic grandeur of the scene was lost to them. They had been robbed of the chief pleasure of their trip to Yosemite Valley. They had been frustrated in their long-cherished design upon Half Dome, and hence were rendered disconsolate and blind to the beauties and the wonders of the place.

Half Dome rears its ice-scarred head fully five thousand feet above the level floor of Yosemite Valley. In the name itself of this great rock lies an accurate and complete description. Nothing more nor less is it than a cyclopean, rounded dome, split in half as cleanly as an apple that is divided by a knife. It is, perhaps, quite needless to state that but one half remains, hence its name, the other half having been carried away by the great ice-river in the stormy time of the Glacial Period. In that dim day one of those frigid rivers gouged a mighty channel from out the solid rock. This channel today is Yosemite Valley. But to return to the Half Dome. On its northeastern side, by circuitous trails and stiff climbing, one may gain the Saddle. Against the slope of the Dome the Saddle leans like a gigantic slab, and from the top of this slab, one thousand feet in length, curves the great circle to the summit of the Dome. A few degrees too steep for unaided climbing, these one thousand feet defied for years the adventurous spirits who fixed yearning eyes upon the crest above.

One day, a couple of clear-headed mountaineers had proceeded to insert iron eye-bolts into holes which they drilled into the rock every few feet apart. But when they found themselves three hundred feet above the Saddle, clinging like flies to the precarious wall with on either hand a yawning abyss, their nerves failed them and they abandoned the enterprise. So it remained for an indomitable Scotchman, one George Anderson, finally to achieve the feat. Beginning where they had left off, drilling and climbing for a week, he had at last set foot upon that awful summit and gazed down into the depths where Mirror Lake reposed, nearly a mile beneath.

In the years which followed, many bold men took advantage of the huge rope ladder which he had put in place; but one winter ladder, cables and all were carried away by the snow and ice. True, most of the eye-bolts, twisted and bent, remained. But few men had since essayed the hazardous undertaking, and of those few more than one gave up his life on the treacherous heights, and not one succeeded.

But Gus Lafee and Hazard Van Dorn had left the smiling valley-land of California and journeyed into the high Sierras, intent on the great adventure. And thus it was that their disappointment was deep and grievous when they awoke on this morning to receive the forestalling message of the little white flag.

"Camped at the foot of the Saddle last night and went up at the first peep of day," Hazard ventured, long after the silent breakfast had been tucked away and the dishes washed.

Gus nodded. It was not in the nature of things that a youth's spirits should long remain at low ebb, and his tongue was beginning to loosen.

"Guess he's down by now, lying in camp and feeling as big as Alexander," the other went on. "And I don't blame him, either; only I wish it were we."

"You can be sure he's down," Gus spoke up at last. "It's mighty warm on that naked rock with the sun beating down on it at this time of year. That was our plan, you know, to go up early and come down early. And any man, sensible enough to get to the top, is bound to have sense enough to do it before the rock gets hot and his hands sweaty."

"And you can be sure he didn't take his shoes with him." Hazard rolled over on his back and lazily regarded the speck of flag fluttering briskly on the sheer edge of the precipice. "Say!" He sat up with a start. "What's that?"

A metallic ray of light flashed out from the summit of Half Dome, then a second and a third. The heads of both boys were craned backward on the instant, agog with excitement.

"What a duffer!" Gus cried. "Why didn't he come down when it was cool?"

Hazard shook his head slowly, as if the question were too deep for immediate answer and they had better defer judgment.

The flashes continued, and as the boys soon noted, at irregular intervals of duration and disappearance. Now they were long, now short; and again they came and went with great rapidity, or ceased altogether for several moments at a time.

"I have it!" Hazard's face lighted up with the coming of understanding. "I have it! That fellow up there is trying to talk to us. He's flashing the sunlight down to us on a pocket-mirror—dot, dash; dot, dash; don't you see?"

The light also began to break in Gus's face. "Ah, I know! It's what they do in war-time—signaling. They call it heliographing, don't they? Same thing as telegraphing, only it's done without wires. And they use the same dots and dashes, too."

"Yes, the Morse alphabet. Wish I knew it."

"Same here. He surely must have something to say to us, or he wouldn't be kicking up all that rumpus."

Still the flashes came and went persistently, till Gus exclaimed: "That chap's in trouble, that's what's the matter with him! Most likely he's hurt himself or something or other."

"Go on!" Hazard scouted.

Gus got out the shotgun and fired both barrels three times in rapid succession. A perfect flutter of flashes came back before the echoes had ceased their antics. So unmistakable was the message that even doubting Hazard was convinced that the man who had forestalled them stood in some grave danger.

"Quick, Gus," he cried, "and pack! I'll see to the horses. Our trip hasn't come to nothing, after all. We've got to go right up Half Dome and rescue him. Where's the map? How do we get to the Saddle?"

"'Taking the horse-trail below the Vernal Falls,'" Gus read from the guide-book, "'one mile of brisk traveling brings the tourist to the world-famed Nevada Fall. Close by, rising up in all its pomp and glory, the Cap of Liberty stands guard—'"

"Skip all that!" Hazard impatiently interrupted. "The trail's what we want."

"Oh, here it is! 'Following the trail up the side of the fall will bring you to the forks. The left one leads to Little Yosemite Valley, Cloud's Rest, and other points.'"

"Hold on; that'll do! I've got it on the map now," again interrupted Hazard. "From the Cloud's Rest trail a dotted line leads off to Half Dome. That shows the trail's abandoned. We'll have to look sharp to find it. It's a day's journey."

"And to think of all that traveling, when right here we're at the bottom of the Dome!" Gus complained, staring up wistfully at the goal.

"That's because this is Yosemite, and all the more reason for us to hurry. Come on! Be lively, now!"

Well used as they were to trail life, but few minutes sufficed to see the camp equipage on the backs of the packhorses and the boys in the saddle. In the late twilight of that evening they hobbled their animals in a tiny mountain meadow, and cooked coffee and bacon for themselves at the very base of the Saddle. Here, also, before they turned into their blankets, they found the camp of the unlucky stranger who was destined to spend the night on the naked roof of the Dome.

Dawn was brightening into day when the panting lads threw themselves down at the summit of the Saddle and began taking off their shoes. Looking down from the great height, they seemed perched upon the ridge-pole of the world, and even the snow-crowned Sierra peaks seemed beneath them. Directly below, on the one hand, lay Little Yosemite Valley, half a mile deep; on the other hand, Big Yosemite, a mile. Already the sun's rays were striking about the adventurers, but the darkness of night still shrouded the two great gulfs into which they peered. And above them, bathed in the full day, rose only the majestic curve of the Dome.

"What's that for?" Gus asked, pointing to a leather-shielded flask which Hazard was securely fastening in his shirt pocket.

"Dutch courage, of course," was the reply. "We'll need all our nerve in this undertaking, and a little bit more, and," he tapped the flask significantly, "here's the little bit more."

"Good idea," Gus commented.

How they had ever come possessed of this erroneous idea, it would be hard to discover; but they were young yet, and there remained for them many uncut pages of life. Believers, also, in the efficacy of whisky as a remedy for snakebite, they had brought with them a fair supply of medicine-chest liquor. As yet they had not touched it.

"Have some before we start?" Hazard asked.

Gus looked into the gulf and shook his head. "Better wait till we get up higher and the climbing is more ticklish."

Some seventy feet above them projected the first eye-bolt. The winter accumulations of ice had twisted and bent it down till it did not stand more than a bare inch and a half above the rock—a most difficult object to lasso at such a distance. Time and again Hazard coiled his lariat in true cowboy fashion and made the cast, and time and again was he baffled by the elusive peg. Nor could Gus do better. Taking advantage of inequalities in the surface, they scrambled twenty feet up the Dome and found they could rest in a shallow crevice. The cleft side of the Dome was so near that they could look over its edge from the crevice and gaze down the smooth, vertical wall for nearly two thousand feet. It was yet too dark down below for them to see farther.

The peg was now fifty feet away, but the path they must cover to get to it was quite smooth, and ran at an inclination of nearly fifty degrees. It seemed impossible, in that intervening space, to find a resting-place. Either the climber must keep going up, or he must slide down; he could not stop. But just here rose the danger. The Dome was sphere-shaped, and if he should begin to slide, his course would be, not to the point from which he had started and where the Saddle would catch him, but off to the south toward Little Yosemite. This meant a plunge of half a mile.

"I'll try it," Gus said simply.

They knotted the two lariats together, so that they had over a hundred feet of rope between them; and then each boy tied an end to his waist.

"If I slide," Gus cautioned, "come in on the slack and brace yourself. If you don't, you'll follow me, that's all!"

"Ay, ay!" was the confident response. "Better take a nip before you start?"

Gus glanced at the proffered bottle. He knew himself and of what he was capable. "Wait till I make the peg and you join me. All ready?"

"Ay."

He struck out like a cat, on all fours, clawing energetically as he urged his upward progress, his comrade paying out the rope carefully. At first his speed was good, but gradually it dwindled. Now he was fifteen feet from the peg, now ten, now eight-but going, oh, so slowly! Hazard, looking up from his crevice, felt a contempt for him and disappointment in him. It did look easy. Now Gus was five feet away, and after a painful effort, four feet. But when only a yard intervened, he came to a standstill—not exactly a standstill, for, like a squirrel in a wheel, he maintained his position on the face of the Dome by the most desperate clawing.

He had failed, that was evident. The question now was, how to save himself. With a sudden, catlike movement he whirled over on his back, caught his heel in a tiny, saucer-shaped depression and sat up. Then his courage failed him. Day had at last penetrated to the floor of the valley, and he was appalled at the frightful distance.

"Go ahead and make it!" Hazard ordered; but Gus merely shook his head.

"Then come down!"

Again he shook his head. This was his ordeal, to sit, nerveless and insecure, on the brink of the precipice. But Hazard, lying safely in his crevice, now had to face his own ordeal, but one of a different nature. When Gus began to slide—as he soon must—would he, Hazard, be able to take in the slack and then meet the shock as the other tautened the rope and darted toward the plunge? It seemed doubtful. And there he lay, apparently safe, but in reality harnessed to death. Then rose the temptation. Why not cast off the rope about his waist? He would be safe at all events. It was a simple way out of the difficulty. There was no need that two should perish. But it was impossible for such temptation to overcome his pride of race, and his own pride in himself and in his honor. So the rope remained about him.

"Come down!" he ordered; but Gus seemed to have become petrified.

"Come down," he threatened, "or I'll drag you down!" He pulled on the rope to show he was in earnest.

"Don't you dare!" Gus articulated through his clenched teeth.

"Sure I will, if you don't come!" Again he jerked the rope.

With a despairing gurgle Gus started, doing his best to work sideways from the plunge. Hazard, every sense on the alert, almost exulting in his perfect coolness, took in the slack with deft rapidity. Then, as the rope began to tighten, he braced himself. The shock drew him half out of the crevice; but he held firm and served as the center of the circle, while Gus, with the rope as a radius, described the circumference and ended up on the extreme southern edge of the Saddle. A few moments later Hazard was offering him the flask.

"Take some yourself," Gus said.

"No; you. I don't need it."

"And I'm past needing it." Evidently Gus was dubious of the bottle and its contents.

Hazard put it away in his pocket. "Are you game," he asked, "or are you going to give it up?"

"Never!" Gus protested. "I am game. No Lafee ever showed the white feather yet. And if I did lose my grit up there, it was only for the moment—sort of like seasickness. I'm all right now, and I'm going to the top."

"Good!" encouraged Hazard. "You lie in the crevice this time, and I'll show you how easy it is."

But Gus refused. He held that it was easier and safer for him to try again, arguing that it was less difficult for his one hundred and sixteen pounds to cling to the smooth rock than for Hazard's one hundred and sixty-five; also that it was easier for one hundred and sixty-five pounds to bring a sliding one hundred and sixteen to a stop than vice versa. And further, that he had the benefit of his previous experience. Hazard saw the justice of this, although it was with great reluctance that he gave in.

Success vindicated Gus's contention. The second time, just as it seemed as if his slide would be repeated, he made a last supreme effort and gripped the coveted peg. By means of the rope, Hazard quickly joined him. The next peg was nearly sixty feet away; but for nearly half that distance the base of some glacier in the forgotten past had ground a shallow furrow. Taking advantage of this, it was easy for Gus to lasso the eye-bolt. And it seemed, as was really the case, that the hardest part of the task was over. True, the curve steepened to nearly sixty degrees above them, but a comparatively unbroken line of eye-bolts, six feet apart, awaited the lads. They no longer had even to use the lasso. Standing on one peg, it was child's play to throw the bight of the rope over the next and to draw themselves up to it.

A bronzed and bearded man met them at the top and gripped their hands in hearty fellowship.

"Talk about your Mont Blancs!" he exclaimed, pausing in the midst of greeting them to survey the mighty panorama. "But there's nothing on all the earth, nor over it, nor under it, to compare with this!" Then he recollected himself and thanked them for coming to his aid. No, he was not hurt or injured in any way. Simply because of his own carelessness, just as he had arrived at the top the previous day, he had dropped his climbing rope. Of course it was impossible to descend without it. Did they understand heliographing? No? That was strange! How did they—

"Oh, we knew something was the matter," Gus interrupted, "from the way you flashed when we fired off the shotgun."

"Find it pretty cold last night without blankets?" Hazard queried.

"I should say so. I've hardly thawed out yet."

"Have some of this." Hazard shoved the flask over to him.

The stranger regarded him quite seriously for a moment, then said,

"My dear fellow, do you see that row of pegs? Since it is my honest intention to climb down them very shortly, I am forced to decline. No, I don't think I'll have any, though I thank you just the same."

Hazard glanced at Gus and then put the flask back in his pocket. But when they pulled the doubled rope through the last eye-bolt and set foot on the Saddle, he again drew out the bottle.

"Now that we're down, we don't need it," he remarked, pithily. "And I've about come to the conclusion that there isn't very much in Dutch courage, after all." He gazed up the great curve of the Dome. "Look at what we've done without it!"

Several seconds thereafter a party of tourists, gathered at the margin of Mirror Lake, were astounded at the unwonted phenomenon of a whisky flask descending upon them like a comet out of a clear sky; and all the way back to the hotel they marveled greatly at the wonders of nature, especially meteorites.

LESSON 7

EXERCISES

Characterization

1. How old do you think Gus and Hazard are? ______

2. What can we tell about their characters by the very fact that they intend to scale Half Dome?
______
______

3. What virtue is shown by their willingness to help the man stranded on top of Half Dome?
______
______

Plot

4. What is the boys' goal, "the chief pleasure," of their trip to Yosemite? ______
______

5. At the beginning of the story, what sight disheartens the boys? Why? ______
______
______

6. What event causes them to continue to climb even though someone has beaten them to the summit? ______
______

7. Do you think Gus and Hazard have much experience with alcohol? ______
______

8. What virtue do they wrongly think that alcohol will give them? ______
______
______

9. Why does the man at the summit refuse the flask when it is offered to him? ______________

____

____

10. Why do you suppose the man's view of "Dutch Courage" differs from that of Gus and Hazard?

____

____

____

11. What do Gus and Hazard discover about themselves at the end of the story? ______________

____

____

12. Two conflicts are present in this story: man versus nature and man versus self. Briefly describe each of these conflicts. ______________

____

____

____

13. What symbolic gesture serves as the resolution of the man versus self conflict? ______________

____

____

Theme

14. Choose the statement that best expresses the theme of this story, and write "theme" next to it. Label the other statements as too general, too specific, or beside the point. You will need to use one of these labels twice.

a. ______________ Virtue must be developed from within—it cannot be applied from without.

b. ______________ The courage to climb mountains does not come from a bottle.

c. ______________ Wisdom comes with age.

d. ______________ Half Dome is a very steep mountain.

e. ______________ Courage is the ability to face your fears.

St. Joan d'Arc

Mary Lynch

Chapter 7

Joan was glad that the French had won Orléans, but also anxious to accomplish the other task God had given her. The Dauphin must be crowned king of France. This would take place at Rheims (Ram). The first French king had been crowned there nine centuries before, as had all French kings since. The Rheims great cathedral also housed holy oil, which had been miraculously brought from Heaven by a dove.

Hundreds upon hundreds of French people came to Rheims for the coronation of Charles VII. All of France knew that it was Joan d'Arc, the Maiden of Orléans, who made it possible.

The coronation was a grand event. Nobility from France and throughout Europe attended the ceremonies. The ladies wore long silk and satin dresses, decorated with ribbons and flowers of every color. There were beautiful flowers in their hair, and even more ribbons. The men wore very colorful clothes, too—long, bright satin jackets and knickers in reds, yellows, greens and blues. They did not wear flowers, but they did have a few ribbons and ruffles at their collars and at their knees for garters. The men wore satin shoes colored to match their clothes. Some had big gold or silver buckles.

The king was dressed impressively, of course. His long jacket and knickers of white satin were pristine, and from his left shoulder to his right hip, he wore a wide white satin sash decorated with many medals. They sparkled with gold and diamonds, and gold buckles with diamonds also glittered on his white satin shoes. His blond, curly hair fell to his shoulders, and he also had a little blond curled mustache and a tiny pointed beard.

Joan was required to wear something special for this wonderful and magnificent occasion as well. The king had ordered the court dressmaker to design a dress especially for her. Joan insisted that she must wear the colors of France, as she had all her life. So she wore a beautiful blue satin dress with tiny white roses around a high neckline, and sleeves to her elbows, with more tiny white roses. A wide, red velvet sash slanted from Joan's right shoulder down her other side to the bottom of her dress. Joan felt a little strange in this elegant dress after wearing her armor for so many months. Her hair was still short, so the dressmaker made a wide band of blue velvet ribbon. She pulled the ribbon up over Joan's forehead, so that her widow's peak showed. Then she brought it back down over Joan's ears and tied it in back with a double bow. She put some tiny white roses above the bow.

Everyone wore beautiful jewelry to the coronation—diamonds, pearls, emeralds, rubies, and sapphires. The king, as a reward for Joan, gave her a special decoration in the form of an eight-pointed, gold star. It was studded with diamonds and sapphires. She wore it on the red sash at her shoulder.

The king's court artist wanted to paint Joan's portrait, but Joan told him she did not have time to sit for him. She would soon be on the battlefield again.

At the coronation ceremony in the cathedral, a choir of one hundred boys' voices combined with a wonderful organ to make the most heavenly music Joan had ever heard.

The solemn procession down to the sanctuary of the cathedral was led by fifty bishops and a cardinal from Rome. They moved with slow, dignified steps. Then came the king. Hanging from his shoulders and draped out behind him was a huge train of dark blue velvet edged with ermine. It was carried by eight ladies of the court. They wore white satin dresses, and on their heads, long veils of white lace.

At the king's side walked the soldier-heroine of France, the Maiden, Joan D'Arc who saved France and who was directly responsible for the coronation. The king had insisted that Joan have the highest place of honor, before any of his ministers. Joan wore a short white lace veil and long white lace gloves. The dressmaker had made a long cape of silver lamé. The ends of it were carried by two young pages, dressed in black velvet. Joan carried the white pennant with which she had been victorious in battle.

Then followed French soldiers in their parade uniforms of dark gray. They carried flags from every province of France, except those under the military control of the English. Other soldiers carried flags from Spain, Italy, Greece, some Catholic countries of Asia, and most importantly, Vatican City in Rome. Then came the knights, carrying their wide-brimmed hats with ostrich plumes, the colors matching their long fancy jackets and breeches. As the procession reached the ceremony, each person sat in his assigned seat.

The king, with Joan at his side, continued forward to the altar and knelt at the bottom step. Joan knelt beside him. The cardinal of France stood on the top step of the sanctuary, waiting to crown the king. First, the cardinal blessed everyone in the cathedral and led them in the Lord's Prayer.

Taking miraculous oil from a golden urn, the cardinal made the sign of the Cross on Charles's forehead. He did the same on Charles's lips and on each of his palms. With each anointing, the cardinal proclaimed:

"With this holy oil, I anoint thee in the name of the Father and of the Son and of the Holy Ghost."

Then he continued, "Charles, do you swear in the Name of Jesus Christ, Who is God, and with your hand on this Holy Bible, that you will serve France with justice and mercy as long as you live?" An acolyte held the huge red book open. Putting his hand on the Holy Bible, Charles answered loudly.

"I do!"

"Charles, do you solemnly swear in God's Holy Name to protect France from danger with all your might?"

"I do!"

Then the cardinal said, "Now, therefore, by the power given to me by our Holy Mother Church, the true and only Church founded by Our Lord and Savior Jesus Christ, I hereby crown you, Charles the Seventh, King of France!"

The cardinal then placed on Charles's head a large golden crown sparkling with jewels, with a large diamond cross on top—the same crown placed on Charlemagne's head centuries before.

Joan knelt in front of the king, with tears in her eyes. She said, "Now the will of God is accomplished."

Then the crowd outside the cathedral roared with joy. "Long live Charles, King of France!"

Ten altar-boys, wearing white lace over red cassocks, entered the sanctuary. They carried large candles in golden candle holders and stood in a row on either side of the altar. The cardinal was then joined by three other priests, followed by four acolytes. The priests wore gold vestments over red cassocks.

The cardinal had worn a mitre on his head for the coronation ceremony. Now he removed it, and handed it to one of the acolytes. Then the cardinal began the prayers at the foot of the altar to begin Mass. A huge triumphant chord from the organ began a joyous Mass of celebration, and then the voices of one hundred boys filled the cathedral.

Later that evening, a grand ball was held in celebration of the coronation. There Joan heard a different kind of music—violins, cellos, flutes, and trumpets. King Charles insisted on dancing with Joan, even though she declared her ignorance of ballroom dancing.

Joan excused herself early from the party. Many of the king's knights wanted to dance with her, but Joan wanted to retire to her room in the castle. She wanted to pray and to listen to her saints.

QUESTIONS

1. What colors does Joan wear for the coronation ceremonies? What does this show about her character? ______________________________

____

2. Why won't Joan sit for her portrait? ______________________________

____

3. Why does Charles give Joan the place of honor at the coronation? ______________________________

____

LESSON 8

"The Gift of the Magi"
O. Henry

One dollar and eighty-seven cents. That was all. And sixty cents of it was in pennies. Pennies saved one and two at a time by bulldozing the grocer and the vegetable man and the butcher until one's cheeks burned with the silent imputation of parsimony that such close dealing implied. Three times Della counted it. One dollar and eighty-seven cents. And the next day would be Christmas.

There was clearly nothing left to do but flop down on the shabby little couch and howl. So Della did it. Which instigates the moral reflection that life is made up of sobs, sniffles, and smiles, with sniffles predominating.

While the mistress of the home is gradually subsiding from the first stage to the second, take a look at the home. A furnished flat at $8 per week. It did not exactly beggar description, but it certainly had that word on the look-out for the mendicancy squad.

In the vestibule below was a letter-box into which no letter would go, and an electric button from which no mortal finger could coax a ring. Also appertaining thereunto was a card bearing the name "Mr. James Dillingham Young."

The "Dillingham" had been flung to the breeze during a former period of prosperity when its possessor was being paid $30 per week. Now, when the income was shrunk to $20, the letters of "Dillingham" looked blurred, as though they were thinking seriously of contracting to a modest and unassuming D. But whenever Mr. James Dillingham Young came home and reached his flat above he was called "Jim" and greatly hugged by Mrs. James Dillingham Young, already introduced to you as Della. Which is all very good.

Della finished her cry and attended to her cheeks with the powder rag. She stood by the window and looked out dully at a grey cat walking a grey fence in a grey backyard. Tomorrow would be Christmas Day, and she had only $1.87 with which to buy Jim a present. She had been saving every penny she could for months, with this result. Twenty dollars a week doesn't go far. Expenses had been greater than she had calculated. They always are. Only $1.87 to buy a present for Jim. Her Jim. Many a happy hour she had spent planning for something nice for him. Something fine and rare and sterling—something just a little bit near to being worthy of the honor of being owned by Jim.

There was a pier-glass between the windows of the room. Perhaps you have seen a pier-glass in an $8 flat. A very thin and very agile person may, by observing his reflection in a rapid sequence of longitudinal strips, obtain a fairly accurate conception of his looks. Della, being slender, had mastered the art.

Suddenly she whirled from the window and stood before the glass. Her eyes were shining brilliantly, but her face had lost its color within twenty seconds. Rapidly she pulled down her hair and let it fall to its full length.

Now, there were two possessions of the James Dillingham Youngs in which they both took a mighty pride. One was Jim's gold watch that had been his father's and his grandfather's. The other was Della's hair. Had the Queen of Sheba lived in the flat across the airshaft, Della would have let her hair hang out of the window some day to dry just to depreciate Her Majesty's jewels and gifts. Had King Solomon been the janitor, with all his treasures piled up in the basement, Jim would have pulled out his watch every time he passed, just to see him pluck at his beard from envy.

So now Della's beautiful hair fell about her, rippling and shining like a cascade of brown waters. It reached below her knee and made itself almost a garment for her. And then she did it up again nervously and quickly. Once she faltered for a minute and stood still while a tear or two splashed on the worn red carpet.

On went her old brown jacket; on went her old brown hat. With a whirl of skirts and with the brilliant sparkle still in her eyes, she cluttered out of the door and down the stairs to the street.

Where she stopped the sign read: "Mme Sofronie. Hair Goods of All Kinds." One flight up Della ran, and collected herself, panting. Madame, large, too white, chilly, hardly looked the "Sofronie."

"Will you buy my hair?" asked Della.

"I buy hair," said Madame. "Take yer hat off and let's have a sight at the looks of it."

Down rippled the brown cascade.

"Twenty dollars," said Madame, lifting the mass with a practised hand.

"Give it to me quick," said Della.

Oh, and the next two hours tripped by on rosy wings. Forget the hashed metaphor. She was ransacking the stores for Jim's present.

She found it at last. It surely had been made for Jim and no one else. There was no other like it in any of the stores, and she had turned all of them inside out. It was a platinum fob chain simple and chaste in design, properly proclaiming its value by substance alone and not by meretricious ornamentation—as all good things should do. It was even worthy of The Watch. As soon as she saw it she knew that it must be Jim's. It was like him. Quietness and value—the description applied to both. Twenty-one dollars they took from her for it, and she hurried home with the 87 cents. With that chain on his watch Jim might be properly anxious about the time in any company. Grand as the watch was, he sometimes looked at it on the sly on account of the old leather strap that he used in place of a chain.

When Della reached home her intoxication gave way a little to prudence and reason.

She got out her curling irons and lighted the gas and went to work repairing the ravages made by generosity added to love. Which is always a tremendous task, dear friends—a mammoth task.

Within forty minutes her head was covered with tiny, close-lying curls that made her look wonderfully like a truant schoolboy. She looked at her reflection in the mirror long, carefully, and critically.

"If Jim doesn't kill me," she said to herself, "before he takes a second look at me, he'll say I look like a Coney Island chorus girl. But what could I do—oh! what could I do with a dollar and eighty-seven cents?"

At 7 o'clock the coffee was made and the frying-pan was on the back of the stove hot and ready to cook the chops.

Jim was never late. Della doubled the fob chain in her hand and sat on the corner of the table near the door that he always entered. Then she heard his step on the stair away down on the first flight, and she turned white for just a moment. She had a habit of saying little silent prayers about the simplest everyday things, and now she whispered: "Please, God, make him think I am still pretty."

The door opened and Jim stepped in and closed it. He looked thin and very serious. Poor fellow, he was only twenty-two—and to be burdened with a family! He needed a new overcoat and he was without gloves.

Jim stepped inside the door, as immovable as a setter at the scent of quail. His eyes were fixed upon Della, and there was an expression in them that she could not read, and it terrified her. It was not anger, nor surprise, nor disapproval, nor horror, nor any of the sentiments that she had been prepared for. He simply stared at her fixedly with that peculiar expression on his face.

Della wriggled off the table and went for him.

"Jim, darling," she cried, "don't look at me that way. I had my hair cut off and sold it because I couldn't have lived through Christmas without giving you a present. It'll grow out again—you won't mind, will you? I just had to do it. My hair grows awfully fast. Say 'Merry Christmas!' Jim, and let's be happy. You don't know what a nice—what a beautiful, nice gift I've got for you."

"You've cut off your hair?" asked Jim, laboriously, as if he had not arrived at that patent fact yet, even after the hardest mental labor.

"Cut it off and sold it," said Della. "Don't you like me just as well, anyhow? I'm me without my hair, ain't I?"

Jim looked about the room curiously.

"You say your hair is gone?" he said, with an air almost of idiocy.

"You needn't look for it," said Della. "It's sold, I tell you—sold and gone, too. It's Christmas Eve, boy. Be good to me, for it went for you. Maybe the hairs of my head were numbered," she went on with a sudden serious sweetness, "but nobody could ever count my love for you. Shall

I put the chops on, Jim?"

Out of his trance Jim seemed quickly to wake. He enfolded his Della. For ten seconds let us regard with discreet scrutiny some inconsequential object in the other direction. Eight dollars a week or a million a year—what is the difference? A mathematician or a wit would give you the wrong answer. The magi brought valuable gifts, but that was not among them. This dark assertion will be illuminated later on.

Jim drew a package from his overcoat pocket and threw it upon the table.

"Don't make any mistake, Dell," he said, "about me. I don't think there's anything in the way of a haircut or a shave or a shampoo that could make me like my girl any less. But if you'll unwrap that package you may see why you had me going a while at first."

White fingers and nimble tore at the string and paper. And then an ecstatic scream of joy; and then, alas! a quick feminine change to hysterical tears and wails, necessitating the immediate employment of all the comforting powers of the lord of the flat.

For there lay The Combs—the set of combs, side and back, that Della had worshipped for long in a Broadway window. Beautiful combs, pure tortoise-shell, with jewelled rims—just the shade to wear in the beautiful vanished hair. They were expensive combs, she knew, and her heart had simply craved and yearned over them without the least hope of possession. And now, they were hers, but the tresses that should have adorned the coveted adornments were gone.

But she hugged them to her bosom, and at length she was able to look up with dim eyes and a smile and say: "My hair grows so fast, Jim!"

And then Della leaped up like a little singed cat and cried, "Oh, oh!"

Jim had not yet seen his beautiful present. She held it out to him eagerly upon her open palm. The dull precious metal seemed to flash with a reflection of her bright and ardent spirit.

"Isn't it a dandy, Jim? I hunted all over town to find it. You'll have to look at the time a hundred times a day now. Give me your watch. I want to see how it looks on it."

Instead of obeying, Jim tumbled down on the couch and put his hands under the back of his head and smiled.

"Dell," said he, "let's put our Christmas presents away and keep 'em a while. They're too nice to use just at present. I sold the watch to get the money to buy your combs. And now suppose you put the chops on."

The magi, as you know, were wise men—wonderfully wise men—who brought gifts to the Babe in the manger. They invented the art of giving Christmas presents. Being wise, their gifts were no doubt wise ones, possibly bearing the privilege of exchange in case of duplication. And here I have lamely related to you the uneventful chronicle of two foolish children in a flat who most unwisely sacrificed for each other the greatest treasures of their house. But in a last word to the wise of these days let it be said that of all who give gifts these two were the wisest. Of all who give and receive gifts, such as they are wisest. Everywhere they are wisest. They are the magi.

LESSON 8

EXERCISES

Characterization

1. Approximately how old do you think Jim and Della are? ______________________________

____

2. Would you describe them as rich, poor, or middle class? Give three examples from the story to support your position. ____

____

____

____

3. What thing does Della prize above all other things? Describe it. ____________________

____

4. What is Jim's most prized possession? Describe it. ______________________________

____

5. From the word bank below, pick out at least three words that describe each character (some words may apply to both characters). Then cite at least one example from the story to support your choice.

arrogant	prayerful	emotional	generous	angry
petty	sympathetic	selfish	even-tempered	

DELLA: ____

____

____

____

JIM: ____

____

____

____

____

6. What two qualities does Della think are exemplified both by the watch chain and by her husband? ______

______

______

Plot

7. As the story opens, Della counts up $1.87 that she has saved. How does she feel about the way she has had to go about saving this money? ______

______

8. When Della sees how little money she has saved, she breaks down and cries. How does this response reflect what we learn about her character as the story progresses? ______

______

______

9. Why is Della upset that she has been able to save so little money? ______

______

10. As Della looks at herself in the mirror, what thought occurs to her? ______

______

11. Does Della act quickly, or does she ponder her course of action for a long time? ______

______

12. What emotion do you think motivates her to make this decision? ______

______

______

13. As Della prepares herself to go on her mission, what does she do that shows us how much of a sacrifice this will involve? ______

______

______

14. How much money is Della able to obtain from Madame Sofronie? ______

______

15. How does Della know when she has found the right present? ______________________________

____

16. How much money does she pay for it? ______________________________________

17. What does she do when she gets home? ______________________________________

____

18. As she waits for her husband to return home, what fears occupy her mind? ______________

____

____

19. What prayer does she say as she hears her husband coming up the stairs? ______________

____

20. When Jim steps inside the door and stares at her, Della is unable to read his expression. What do you think is going through Jim's mind at this point? ______________________________

____

____

21. What emotion does Della think Jim is experiencing as he repeatedly asks about her hair?

____

____

22. Once he is over the initial shock, what does Jim do? ______________________________

____

23. What does this show us about his character? ______________________________________

____

____

24. Imagine for a moment that Jim is a selfish person who has bought a gift for his wife only because it was Christmas and he had to. What might his reaction have been when he saw what Della had done to her hair? ______________________________________

____

____

____

25. When Della opens the present from Jim, she begins to cry hysterically. Why does she react in this way? ____

____

____

26. What does Della remember that causes her to forget her sorrow? ______________________

____

27. What does this show us about her character? ______________________________

____

28. What is Jim's reaction when he sees Della's gift? ______________________________

____

29. What emotion do you think he feels that overwhelms any disappointment he experiences at not being able to use the gift? ______________________________

____

30. At the climax of the action, Jim and Della face the fact that they have given up their most valued possessions in order to buy gifts that are useless to the possessor. They briefly struggle with feelings of sorrow and frustration, but their love for one another soon restores them to serenity. Into which category of conflict would you place this struggle? ______________

____

31. Quote the words that Jim speaks that serve as the resolution of the conflict, indicating that all will be well: ____

____

____

____

32. What noun-adjective pair does the narrator use to describe the magi in the last paragraph?

____

____

33. What noun-adjective pair does the narrator use to describe Jim and Della in the last paragraph?

____

____

34. What gifts did the magi bring to Jesus (Matthew 2:11)? ______________________________

____

____

35. Which do you think were worth more money: the gifts of the magi or the gifts that Jim and Della gave to each other? ______________________________

____

36. The narrator tells us that the magi gave wise gifts, and humorously suggests that they had wisely planned things so that Jesus would be able to exchange his gifts if necessary. How does this contrast with the gift-giving of Jim and Della? ______________________________

____

____

37. At the end of the story, Jim and Della go on living happily in spite of their gift-giving disaster. What is the real gift that each gave the other? ______________________________

____

38. Do you think they give this gift to each other only on Christmas Day? ______________________________

____

39. Earlier in the story, the narrator commented "The magi brought valuable gifts, but that was not among them. This dark assertion will be illuminated later on." Do you see the meaning of this statement now? Explain it in your own words. ______________________________

____

____

Theme

40. Choose the statement below that most accurately expresses the overall theme of the "The Gift of the Magi." Then label the other statements as too general, too specific, or beside the point. You will not use all the choices.

a. ____________________ The gift of self gives meaning to all other gifts.

b. ____________________ Christmas is a time for giving gifts.

c. ____________________ Love conquers all.

St. Joan d'Arc

Mary Lynch

Chapter 8

When King Charles asked Joan to name a reward for her victories, she answered, "Do not tax Domremy any more!" The king immediately complied. In addition, he proclaimed Joan and her family to be formally installed as nobility.

God's messages had not included any instructions for France or for Joan following the coronation. Now, however, the French generals and soldiers were eager to continue fighting. They wanted to drive the English from France completely and immediately. Joan wanted the English out of France, too, but she had received no orders from her saints about further fighting. Just the same, the French generals persuaded her to lead them in a battle to free Paris from the English and the Burgundian troops who controlled it. The duke of Burgundy had sided with King Henry VI of England. He was a traitor to his country.

Sadly, the French lost the battle for Paris, and Joan was captured. At first, she was held prisoner in a large castle and guarded by soldiers of Burgundy. The castle was not far from where the English were still fighting the French. Though she was a prisoner, Joan was given reports of the daily skirmishes. Her heart sank at the news, for the French lost every battle, and the English destroyed every town they conquered. They even killed infants and children. In prison, Joan's heart ached for her country.

King Charles should have come to Joan's rescue, or at least offered ransom for her, but he did not. Instead, the newly-crowned king retreated to southern France with his noblemen. He valued his own safety more than Joan's.

The Burgundian churchmen, led by Bishop Pierre Cauchon (koh-shown), were traitors to France and to Holy Mother Church. Cauchon was ambitious; as a bishop, he had great wealth which he wanted to protect and to increase. He plotted with the duke of Burgundy because he thought England would conquer France, and he wanted to be on the winning side of the war.

He knew he would please the English and the duke by destroying Joan d'Arc. They did not want her to lead the French soldiers to victory. They wanted her to be burned at the stake as a heretic. To weaken Joan's reputation, Cauchon and the other traitorous churchmen claimed that she was a witch and had conversations with the devil. They told Joan that if she did not confess to being a witch, they would not allow her to receive Confession and Communion.

"I am in danger of death," she replied, "and want to be allowed to make my Confession, receive the Body of my Savior and be buried in consecrated ground." Despite Joan's yearning to receive the sacraments, Cauchon continued to refuse them to her. During this period, she was greatly comforted by her saints.

At the time of Joan's capture, she was wearing her armor. Her soldier's attire required that she wear men's under clothing rather than petticoats, and even after being in prison, Joan continued to wear pants. She remained a soldier of France and of God. Cauchon tried to twist Joan's motives for staying in her soldier's clothes; he argued that wearing men's clothing was sinful.

The Burgundian churchmen pretended they would give Joan a fair trial, but they ignored much evidence in her favor. At one point in her trial, Joan asked Cauchon, "Why do you write everything down that is against me, and nothing that is for me?" She requested that she be sent to Rome to receive a just trial, but the French bishops refused. They knew that if Rome saw the truth of Joan's words, she would be freed and praised.

For many months, they kept Joan in handcuffs and leg irons. Her prison cell was dark and dirty, and the guards were cruel. One time, Cauchon told her that they would torture her and force the truth out of her. Soldiers took her to the torture cell, which was filled with many instruments of torture—contraptions made of iron and rope, nails and fire. At the sight of these devices, however, Joan seemed to grow in strength.

She said, "If you were to tear my limbs apart and drive my soul from my body, I could not say anything different; and if I did, I should declare afterward that you had made me say it by force!" So, the traitors decided not to torture her.

When Cauchon sent a report to the Pope in Rome, it was full of lies. He declared that she was a heretic who had not taken back anything she said against God and the Church. A canon lawyer named Jean Lohier (Loh-yair) investigated Joan's trial and formally declared it illegal and unfair. He announced:

"This trial is not following the regular and proper procedure of such trials. No written charges [accusations] have been produced... She has no lawyer... Most of the people at the trial are spurred on by hatred. I will take no further part in this business..." And he returned to Paris. Joan's trial continued.

Joan was in prison for more than a year. She suffered greatly, but she offered her suffering for the souls in Purgatory. Once, when Cauchon questioned her, Joan said to him, "Take good heed of what you do, because I am truly sent from God, and you are putting yourself in great peril!"

As a result of Cauchon's lies and unfair method of trial, Joan was declared a heretic. The penalty for being a heretic was to be burned alive.

Just before her execution, Joan was allowed Confession and Communion. At this point, her reception of the sacraments would not influence the outcome of her trial, so Cauchon agreed to allow it.

Early on the morning of Wednesday, May 30, 1431, Joan was brought out of prison in a high, wooden two-wheeled cart. She was taken to the square in the middle of the town. All the way there, people lined the streets and hung out of their windows, calling to "Saint Joan!" for her blessing.

The square was packed with people, all lamenting loudly. After being in prison for a year, Joan had lost the color in her cheeks. Her face was thin and gaunt. Her beautiful blue eyes were shadowed. She looked terribly tired, and her shoulders drooped. Her beautiful black hair that had been shiny and well-kept now fell dully to her shoulders. She could not smile, even when the people called blessings to her. Joan looked so pale and forlorn that a groan went up from the crowd.

Then shouts began: "Joan the Maiden of Orléans!" "Saint Joan!" "Joan, pray for us!" "Joan! Saint of France!" The English soldiers threatened the patriotic crowd into silence with their swords and tried to protect the traitors of Burgundy from them.

Joan wore the long brown robe given to heretics to receive their punishment. There were two platforms at the sides of the square. Joan was taken to one of these. On the other platform stood the Church "judges." They announced that Joan was a heretic and added, "We pray the secular power will be moderate in its judgment of you."

The word "secular" means the non-church government. The wicked Church leaders called Joan a heretic, but would not declare judgment against her. At this point in history, the Church and civil authorities worked together. Judgment and physical punishment for sin were the responsibilities of secular governments.

The chief of police waved to the soldiers holding Joan, saying, "Take her!" So they took her to the stake and chained her to it. The stake was made of plaster and raised high above the ground. It was surrounded by piles of straw, planks, tree limbs, and brambles.

One of the priests gave a sermon as the soldiers chained Joan to the stake. Joan prayed without ceasing and asked the priests standing nearby to say Mass for her. She said to the judges, "I beg all of you standing here to forgive any harm I have done, as I forgive you harm you have done me!"

The crowds surrounded the stake, still calling to Joan. "Joan, the Maiden of Orléans! Pray for us!" "Joan, Savior of France! Pray for us!"

Many were saying the Our Father and the Hail Mary. Nearly all were crying. These were true Frenchmen who loved their country, loved their king, and loved Joan, savior of both.

Joan prayed for help from St. Michael. She told the crowd that her voices came from God, and that all they said was true. She asked for a crucifix, and a nearby soldier held one up to her.

"Please keep holding it up where I can see it!" begged Joan. Then the executioner lit the hay and wood. Smoke began curling up to Joan's face. The wood caught fire and began to crackle all around her. The smoke was billowing thickly. All could hear Joan calling Our Lord's Holy Name.

"Jesus! Jesus! Jesus!" St. Michael came to Joan's assistance as the thick smoke stifled her cries. Unable to breathe, Joan lost consciousness quickly and was spared the pain of the flames. By the time the fire reached her body, she was already in Heaven with Our Lord.

All Frenchmen were sure that Joan was a saint. Now, it seemed as if Joan was still conducting the war against the English by her intercession. The French duke of Burgundy and his army turned against their English friends. Even though the English crowned their own King Henry as king of France, the French battled them and drove them completely out of France. This was the end of what is called the "Hundred Year War" which we mentioned at the beginning of our story.

The French King Charles VII, whom Joan had succeeded in having crowned king, was now finally doing what he should have done long before. He decided to see that Joan was no longer called a heretic by the Church. He published a formal declaration:

"Joan d'Arc was executed unjustly, most cruelly, and against reason."

Charles ordered that the truth about the trial be told everywhere. Having cleared Joan of wrongdoing, Charles succeeded in having Holy Mother Church make a complete study of Joan's trial. The Church totally removed all accusations against Joan, saying it was all fraud.

In May 1920, four hundred years after she lost her life in flames, Joan was canonized a saint by Holy Mother Church. Joan's obedience to God led her to Heaven and France to freedom.

If Joan had failed to obey God, France would not have been free at the time of the American Revolution. Like France, the American colonies fought for their independence from England. George Washington thought France would thus be a good ally for the colonies in their revolution. He sent Benjamin Franklin to ask France for help. The French remembered the Hundred Years' War and came to our aid. If Joan of Arc had not been obedient to God, however, France would have been unable to help the colonies, and the United States might not exist today.

Holy Mother Church has dedicated America to Mary under her title "The Immaculate Conception." America is, therefore, under the Blessed Mother's special protection. With her intercession, the United States may accomplish great things in God's Will. We should follow St. Joan's example of obedience.

St. Joan of Arc, pray for us!

QUESTIONS

1. What motivates Cauchon to try Joan as a heretic? Please explain. ______________________

2. How does Joan respond to the cruelty of her captors? ______________________

3. Even though her captors succeed in burning Joan at the stake as a heretic, she is triumphant. Please explain. ______________________

Notes

Notes

Notes

Notes

Notes